FUNNY RHYMES

Collected by Barbara Ireson

Illustrated by Lesley Smith

Beaver Books

A Beaver Book
Published by Arrow Books Limited
62–65 Chandos Place, London WC2N 4NW
An imprint of Century Hutchinson Limited

London · Melbourne · Sydney · Auckland
Johannesburg and agencies throughout
the world

Beaver edition 1980
Reprinted 1988 (twice) and 1989 (twice)

Set in Garamond

Printed and bound in Great Britain by
Cox & Wyman Ltd, Reading

ISBN 0 09 959380 7

Contents

What a crowd! 7

Family and friends 30

Oh, what a pity! 46

Animal fair 62

Fancy that! 79

Me, myself and I 97

Yum, yum! 112

There and back again 130

Acknowledgements 149

Index of titles 151

Index of first lines 156

What a crowd!

A little girl I hate

I saw a little girl I hate
And kicked her with my toes.
She turned
And smiled
And KISSED me!
Then she punched me in the nose.

Arnold Spilka

Sulky Sue

Here's Sulky Sue;
What shall we do?
Turn her face to the wall
Till she comes to.

Anon

Queen, Queen Caroline

Queen, Queen Caroline
Dipped her hair in turpentine;
Turpentine made it shine,
Queen, Queen Caroline.

Anon

Cry-baby

A cry-baby whimpers wherever she goes.
She cries if a pussycat steps on her toes,
Or a ladybug lights on the end of her nose.
  Boohoo! Boohoo! Boohoo!

A cry-baby weeps if she can't have her way.
She screams and she yells for the rest of the day.
She'd much rather whine than dine or play.
  Boohoo! Boohoo! Boohoo!

A cry-baby sobs if her mother says 'No –
You cannot stay up for a late TV show.
It's past nine o'clock – to bed you must go.'
  Boohoo! Boohoo! Boohoo!

The least little thing makes a cry-baby bawl,
Like bumping her knee on a chair in the hall.
Indeed, she will wail over nothing at all.
  Boohoo! Boohoo! Boohoo!

Martin Gardner

Tony Baloney

Tony Baloney is fibbing again –
Look at him wiggle and try to pretend.
Tony Baloney is telling a lie:
Phony old Tony Baloney, goodbye!

Dennis Lee

The way to the zoo

That's the way to the zoo,
That's the way to the zoo,
The monkey house is nearly full
But there's room enough for you.

Anon

The Young Lady whose nose

There was a Young Lady whose nose
Was so long that it reached to her toes;
   So she hired an old lady,
   Whose conduct was steady,
To carry that wonderful nose.

Edward Lear

The old man with a beard

There was an old man with a beard,
Who said, 'It is just as I feared —
Two owls and a hen, four larks and a wren
Have all built their nests in my beard.'

Edward Lear

Timothy Titus

Timothy Titus took two ties
To tie two tups to two tall trees,
To terrify the terrible Thomas a Tullamees.
How many Ts in *that*?

Anon

John

John could take his clothes off
but could not put them on.

His patient mother dressed him,
and said to little John,

'Now, John! You keep your things on.'
But John had long since gone –

and left a trail of sneakers
and small things in the sun,

so she would know to find him
wherever he might run.

And at the end of every trail
stood Mrs Jones and Son,

she with all his little clothes
and little John – with none!

For John could take his clothes off
but could not put them on.

His patient mother dressed him
and on went little John –
and on –
    and on –
        and on –

N. M. Bodecker

There was a crooked man

There was a crooked man, and he walked a crooked mile;
He found a crooked sixpence against a crooked stile;
He bought a crooked cat, which caught a crooked mouse;
And they all lived together in a little crooked house.

Anon

Two witches

There was a witch
The witch had an itch
The itch was so itchy it
Gave her a twitch.

Another witch
Admired the twitch
So she started twitching
Though she had no itch.

Now both of them twitch
So it's hard to tell which
Witch has the itch and
Which witch has the twitch.

Alexander Reznikoff

The Emperor's rhyme

The King of Peru
(Who was Emperor too)
  Had a sort of a rhyme
    Which was useful to know,
If he felt very shy
When a stranger came by,
  Or they asked him the time
    When his watch didn't go;
Or supposing he fell
(By mistake) down a well,
  Or tumbled when skating
    And sat on his hat,
Or perhaps wasn't told,
Till his porridge was cold –
  That his breakfast was waiting –
    Or something like that;

Oh, whenever the Emperor
Got into a temper, or
  Felt himself sulky or sad,
He would murmur and murmur,
Until he felt firmer,
  This curious rhyme which he had:

Eight eights are sixty-four
    Multiply by seven.
When it's done,
Carry one
    And take away eleven.
Nine nines are eighty-one
    Multiply by three.
If it's more,
Carry four,
    And then it's time for tea.

So whenever the Queen
Took his armour to clean,
   And she didn't remember
    To use any starch;
Or his birthday (in May)
Was a horrible day,
   Being wet as November
    And windy as March;
Or, if sitting in state
With the Wise and the Great,
   He just happened to hiccup
    While signing his name,
Or the Queen gave a cough,
When his crown tumbled off
   As he bent to pick up
    A pen for the same;

Oh, whenever the Emperor
Got into a temper, or
   Felt himself awkward and shy,
He would whisper and whisper,
Until he felt crisper,
   This odd little rhyme to the sky.

   Eight eights are eighty-one;
    Multiply by seven.
   If it's more,
   Carry four,
    And take away eleven.
   Nine nines are sixty-four;
    Multiply by three.
   When it's done,
   Carry one,
    And then it's time for tea.

A. A. Milne

A grenadier

Who comes here?
  A grenadier.
What do you want?
  A pot of beer.
Where's your money?
  I forgot it.
Get you gone,
  You silly blockhead.

Anon

The girl in the lane

The girl in the lane
That couldn't speak plain,
Cried, 'Gobble, gobble, gobble!'
The man on the hill
That couldn't stand still,
Went hobble, hobble, hobble!

Anon

My first suitor

Little Jack Dandy-prat
  Was my first suitor;
He had a dish and spoon
  And a little pewter;
He'd linen and woollen,
  And woollen and linen,
A little pig on a string
  Cost him five shilling.

Anon

The fat man of Bombay

There was a fat man of Bombay
Who was smoking one sunshiny day
  When a bird called a Snipe
  Flew away with his pipe,
Which vexed the fat man of Bombay.

Anon

Robin the Bobbin

Robin the Bobbin, the big fat Ben,
He ate more meat than fourscore men;
He ate a cow, he ate a calf,
He ate a butcher and a half;
He ate a church, he ate a steeple,
He ate the priest and all the people.
A cow and a calf,
An ox and a half,
A church and a steeple,
And all the good people,
Then Robin the Bobbin, the big fat Ben,
Sat down at the table to start again.
He ate . . .

Anon

Little Dimity

Poor little pigeon-toed Dimity Drew,
The more she ate, the smaller she grew.
When some people eat, they get taller and taller;
When Dimity ate, she got smaller and smaller.
She went for a walk, and all you could see
Was a tam-o'-shanter the size of a pea,
An umbrella as big as the cross on a T,
And a wee pocketbook of butterfly blue.
She came to a crack one half an inch wide,
Tripped on a breadcrumb, fell inside,
And slowly disappeared from view.

William Jay Smith

The Old Man on the Border

There was an Old Man on the Border,
Who lived in the utmost disorder;
　　He danced with the Cat,
　　And made Tea in his Hat,
Which vexed all the folks on the border.

Edward Lear

The Young Lady whose chin

There was a Young Lady whose chin
Resembled the point of a pin;
　　So she had it made sharp,
　　And purchased a harp,
And played several tunes with her chin.

Edward Lear

Sue, Sue

Sue, Sue, what would you do
If a grasshopper ate a hole in your shoe?

Gaye, Gaye, what would you say
If a ladybird nibbled your socks away?

Barbara Ireson

Hurry-Scurry

Hurry-Scurry
Had a worry,
No one liked
His pepper curry,
Burnt his fingers in the pot,
Pepper curry's far too hot.

Cynthia Mitchell

Dicky Dan

Dicky Dan was a funny old man,
He washed his head in a cooking pan,
He combed his hair with the leg of a chair,
Dicky Dan was a funny old man.

Anon

What is the rhyme for porringer?

What is the rhyme for porringer?
What is the rhyme for porringer?
The King he had a daughter fair
And gave the Prince of Orange her.

Anon

Seven fat fishermen

Seven fat fishermen,
Sitting side by side,
Fished from a bridge,
By the banks of the Clyde.

The first caught a tiddler,
The second caught a crab,
The third caught a winkle,
The fourth caught a dab.

The fifth caught a tadpole,
The sixth caught an eel,
But the seventh, he caught
An old cart-wheel.

Anon

Have you heard of the man?

Have you heard of the man
   Who stood on his head,
And put his clothes
   Into his bed,
And folded himself
   On a chair instead?

Anon

People

Hour after hour,
In many places,
People sit,
Making faces.

William Jay Smith

The abominable snowman

I've never seen an abominable snowman,
I'm hoping not to see one,
I'm also hoping, if I do,
That it will be a wee one.

Ogden Nash

Big Gumbo

Great big gawky Gumbo Cole
Couldn't stop growing to save his soul.
Gave up eating, gave up drink,
Sat in the closet, hoped to shrink;
But he grew and grew till he burst the door,
His head went through to the upper floor,
His feet reached down to the cellar door.
He grew still more till the house came down
And Gumbo Cole stepped out on the town
And smashed it in like an old anthill!
Never stopped growing, never will,
Ten times as tall as a telephone pole,
Too big for his breeches – Gumbo Cole!

William Jay Smith

Skididdle, Skidaddle

Skididdle,
Skidaddle,
Joe's in a muddle.
He doesn't know which end's up.
He's wrapped his ears in a pair of socks
And stuck his foot in a cup.

Susanna Steele

Cavendish McKellar

Cavendish McKellar,
Clever little feller,
Bought himself a new umbrella,
Rubber boots and new galoshes,
Plastic hats and macintoshes –
All to stop his mother's grizzles
When he frolicked in the drizzles.

Alas, his troubles were in vain.
But why?
      It didn't rain.

Peter Wesley-Smith

Jerry and Mandy

Jerry Hall,
He is so small,
A rat could eat him,
Hat and all.

Mandy Hall,
She is so tall,
She makes the Eiffel Tower
Look small.

Variation on an old rhyme by Barbara Ireson

Deborah Delora

Deborah Delora, she liked a bit of fun;
She went to the baker's and she bought a penny bun;
Dipped the bun in treacle and threw it at her teacher –
Deborah Delora! What a wicked creature!

Anon

A big, fat lady

Christopher Columbus!
What do you think of that?
A big fat lady
Sat upon my hat.

Christopher Columbus!
What do you think of that?
The big fat lady
Has squashed my hat quite flat!

Anon

Bushrangers

Fifty burly bushrangers
    Went out to steal some gold;
But all the bush was wet with dew
    And one caught a cold.
And one found a bulldog ant
    Creeping on his chest;
And one had a 'gammy' leg
    And had to have a rest.
One thought he saw a snake,
    Another had a pain;
The rest, they heard a gun go off,
    And scampered home again.

Isobel Kendall Bowden

Old Mrs Lazibones

Old Mrs Lazibones
And her dirty daughter
Never used soap
And never used water.
> Higgledy piggledy cowpat
> What d'you think of that?

Daisies from their fingernails,
Birds' nests in their hair-O,
Dandelions from their ears, —
What a dirty pair-O!
> Higgledy piggledy cowpat
> What d'you think of that?

Came a prince who sought a bride,
Riding past their doorstep,
Quick, said Mrs Lazibones.
Girl, under the watertap.
> Higgledy piggledy cowpat
> What d'you think of that?

Washed her up and washed her down,
Then she washed her sideways,
But the prince was far, far away,
He'd ridden off on the highways.
> Higgledy piggledy cowpat
> What d'you think of that?

Gerda Mayer

A man and his hat

There was an old man
Who was fond of his hat
It was battered and shabby
But he would get crabby
If searching around
It could not be found.
He'd look all about
And he'd call and he'd shout:
'Just where is my hat?
It was here where I sat,
It was here yesterday
Did you take it away?
Where's my hat, where's my
   hat?
It was here where I sat.'

He would rave, he would roar
And go out through the door,
Calling out to his wife
Who was used to such strife:
'I put it just there
Quite close to my chair,
When I came in from walking
And we sat there talking.'

Now, his wife was quite nice
So she said to him twice,
'Please calm yourself dear!
Your hat's somewhere here!
I will find it for you,
Don't get into a stew.'

Well, she looked everywhere
Both up and down stairs
But no hat could she find
Not the old battered kind,
And the man kept on saying,
'I do want my hat,
It was here where I sat
Just here near the cat.'

The house-cat was sleeping
All comfy and snug
Curled up like a ball
On the woolly hearthrug,
But the man and his wife
With their clatter and strife
Had disturbed the poor cat
All because of the hat
Which couldn't be found
It was nowhere around.

Opening one eye then two
Wondering what next they'd do,
Pussy slowly stretched out
Leaving neither in doubt . . .
'LOOK! there is the hat
Why it's squashed nearly flat!'
Then they pushed at the cat
And they grabbed at the hat . . .
But the cat did not mind
He knew they were kind.

The man put on his hat
And he patted the cat
And his face changed completely
As he smiled discreetly,
And he thanked his dear wife
And said she was nice
Then went out for a walk
Without further talk.

The pussy went too
What else could she do?

Letitia Parr

29

Family and friends

The visitor

it came today to visit
and moved into the house
it was smaller than an elephant
but larger than a mouse

first it slapped my sister
then it kicked my dad
then it pushed my mother
oh! that really made me mad

it went and tickled rover
and terrified the cat
it sliced apart my necktie
and rudely crushed my hat

it smeared my head with honey
and filled the tub with rocks
and when i yelled in anger
it stole my shoes and socks

that's just the way it happened
it happened all today
before it bowed politely
and softly went away.

Jack Prelutsky

Dad and the cat and the tree

This morning a cat got
Stuck in our tree.
Dad said, 'Right, just
Leave it to me.'

The tree was wobbly,
The tree was tall.
Mum said, 'For goodness'
Sake don't fall.'

'Fall?' scoffed Dad,
'A climber like me?
Child's play, this is!
You wait and see.'

He got out the ladder
From the garden shed.
It slipped. He landed
In the flower bed.

'Never mind,' said Dad,
Brushing the dirt
Off his hair and his face
And his trousers and his shirt,

'We'll try Plan B. Stand
Out of the way!'
Mum said, 'Don't fall
Again, O.K.?'

'Fall again?' said Dad.
'Funny joke!'
Then he swung himself up
On a branch. It broke.

Dad landed *wallop*
Back on the deck.
Mum said, 'Stop it,
You'll break your neck!'

'Rubbish!' said Dad.
'Now we'll try Plan C.
Easy as winking
To a climber like me!'

Then he climbed up high
On the garden wall.
Guess what?
He *didn't fall!*

He gave a great leap
And he landed flat
In the crook of the tree-trunk –
Right on the cat!

The cat gave a yell
And sprang to the ground,
Pleased as Punch to be
Safe and sound.

So it's smiling and smirking,
Smug as can be,
But poor old Dad's
Still

Stuck
Up
The
Tree!

Kit Wright

Neighbours

Mrs Down
Went to town
With her face
Painted brown.

Mrs Jack,
She came back
With her husband
In a sack.

Mrs Green
Was last seen
Getting in
A space machine.

Mrs White
Got a fright
When she met
A ghost last night.

Mrs Brain
Stole a plane
And she flew
Away to Spain.

Mrs Binn
Got so slim
She looked like
A long thin pin.

Mrs Pratt
Got so fat
She took up two chairs
When down she sat.

Mrs Mast
Was the last
So she jumped on a train
As it rumbled past.

Barbara Ireson

Brother

I had a little brother
And I brought him to my mother
And I said I want another
Little brother for a change.

But she said don't be a bother
So I took him to my father
And I said this little bother
Of a brother's very strange.

But he said one little brother
Is exactly like another
And every little brother
Misbehaves a bit he said.

So I took the little bother
From my mother and my father
And I put the little bother
Of a brother back to bed.

Mary Ann Hoberman

My party

My parents said I could have a party
And that's just what I did.

Dad said, 'Who had you thought of inviting?'
I told him. He said, 'Well, you'd better start writing,'
And that's just what I did.

To:
Phyllis Willis, Horace Morris,
Nancy, Clancy, Bert and Gert Sturt,
Dick and Mick and Nick Crick,
Ron, Don, John,
Dolly, Molly, Polly –
Neil Peel –
And my dear old friend, Dave Dirt.

I wrote, 'Come along, I'm having a party,'
And that's just what they did.

They all arrived with huge appetites
As Dad and I were fixing the lights.
I said, 'Help yourself to the drinks and bites!'
And that's just what they did,
All of them:

Phyllis Willis, Horace Morris,
Nancy, Clancy, Bert and Gert Sturt,
Dick and Mick and Nick Crick,
Ron, Don, John,
Dolly, Molly, Polly —
Neil Peel —
And my dear old friend, Dave Dirt.

Now, I had a good time and as far as I could tell
The party seemed to go pretty well —
Yes, that's just what it did.

Then Dad said, 'Come on, just for fun,
Let's have a *turn* from everyone!'
And a turn's just what they did,

All of them:

Phyllis Willis, Horace Morris,
Nancy, Clancy, Bert and Gert Sturt,
Dick and Mick and Nick Crick,
Ron, Don, John,
Dolly, Molly, Polly —
Neil Peel —
And my dear old friend, Dave Dirt.

Phyllis and Clancy
And Horace and Nancy
Did a song and dance number
That was really fancy —

Dolly, Molly, Polly,
Ron, Don and John
Performed a play
That went on and on and on —

Gert and Bert Sturt,
Sister and brother,
Did an imitation of
Each other.

(Gert Sturt put on Bert Sturt's shirt
And Bert Sturt put on Gert Sturt's skirt.)

Neil Peel
All on his own
Danced an eightsome reel.

Dick and Mick
And Nicholas Crick
Did a most *ingenious*
Conjuring trick.

And my dear old friend, Dave Dirt,
Was terribly sick
All over the flowers.
We cleaned it up.
It took *hours*.

But as Dad said, giving a party's not easy.
You really
Have to
Stick at it.
I agree. And if Dave gives a party
I'm certainly
Going to be
Sick at it.

Kit Wright

Five little piggies

My little
dad
had
five little piggies:
good 'un,
bad 'un,
gay 'un,
sad 'un
and one little piggie
who was
mad
  mad
      mad!
Five little piggies
had
my little
dad.

Translated from a Danish nursery
rhyme by N. M. Bodecker

I have a friend

I have a friend who keeps on standing on her hands.
That's fine,
Except I find it very difficult to talk to her
Unless I stand on mine.

Karla Kuskin

Brothers

Andrew is my brother
And I've another brother,
He's called Lee
And then there's me –
We're TRIPLETS –
Oh, poor Mother!

Barbara Ireson

Mr Tom Narrow

A scandalous man
   Was Mr Tom Narrow,
He pushed his grandmother
   Round in a barrow.
And he called out loud
   As he rang his bell,
'Grannies to sell!
   Old grannies to sell!'

The neighbours said,
   As they passed them by,
'This poor old lady
   We will not buy.
He surely must be
   A mischievous man
To try for to sell
   His own dear Gran.'

'Besides,' said another,
   'If you ask me,
She'd be very small use
   That I can see.'
'You're right,' said a third,
   'And no mistake –
A very poor bargain
   She'd surely make.'

So Mr Tom Narrow
   He scratched his head,
And he sent his grandmother
   Back to bed;
And he rang his bell
   Through all the town
Till he sold his barrow
   For half a crown.

James Reeves

For sale

One sister for sale!
One sister for sale!
One crying and spying young sister for sale!
I'm really not kidding,
So who'll start the bidding?
Do I hear a dollar?
A nickel?
A penny?
Oh, isn't there, isn't there, isn't there any
One kid who will buy this old sister for sale,
This crying and spying young sister for sale?

Shel Silverstein

Dad's beard

Last year my Dad grew a great big thick red beard:
Mum made him.
Can't think how in the world she managed
To persuade him.

Nothing but hair
Everywhere:
       Can't say I liked it at all.
But now he's shaved it,
I wonder:
Should he have saved it?

It's odd. Did Dad look better with his beard?
I doubt it.
But he certainly looks pretty weird
Without it.
       Nothing but face
       All over the place:
              Can't say I like it at all.

                              Kit Wright

42

Granny in the kitchen

Granny in the kitchen,
Doing a bit of stitching,
In comes a bogie man,
And chases Granny out.
Ah, says Granny, that's not fair,
Ah, says the bogie man, I don't care.

Anon

The pasty

Deedle deedle dumpling, my son John
Ate a pasty five feet long;
He bit it once, he bit it twice,
Oh, my goodness, it was full of mice!

Anon

Saturday night

On Saturday night I lost my
wife,
And where do you think I
found her?
Up in the moon, singing a
tune
With all the stars around
her.

Anon

43

Dreadful

Someone ate the baby,
It's rather sad to say.
Someone ate the baby
So she won't be out to play.
    We'll never hear her whiney cry
    Or have to feel if she is dry.
    We'll never hear her asking 'Why?'
    Someone ate the baby.

Someone ate the baby.
It's absolutely clear
Someone ate the baby
'Cause the baby isn't here.
    We'll give away her toys and clothes.
    We'll never have to wipe her nose.
    Dad says, 'That's the way it goes.'
    Someone ate the baby.

Someone ate the baby.
What a frightful thing to eat!
Someone ate the baby
Though she wasn't very sweet.
    It was a heartless thing to do.
    The policemen haven't got a clue.
    I simply can't imagine who
    Would go and (burp) eat the baby.

Shel Silverstein

The Elephant

Aunt Mary is my aunt,
    She took me to the Zoo.
She offered to the Elephant
    One bun – it wanted two.

Aunt Mary had a hat
    All cherries on her head.
The beast thought 'Buns are good, but that
    Will do quite well instead.'

The creature smiled serene,
    And made a little bow . . .
Aunt Mary's never, never seen
    Her hat from then to now.

Aunt Mary danced a jig,
    And wept till she was blind,
And screamed, 'You bad, old, ugly pig!'
    But, it didn't seem to mind.

John Joy Bell

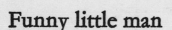

Funny little man

A little man I used to see
Liked to come to tea with me,
But he never brought his head,
He left his head in bed instead.

Barbara Ireson

Oh, what a pity!

The young man of Bengal

There was a young man of Bengal
Who went to a fancy-dress ball.
    He went just for fun
    Dressed up as a bun,
And a dog ate him up in the hall.

Anon

A pig tale

        Poor Jane Higgins,
        She had five piggins,
And one got drowned in the Irish Sea.
        Poor Jane Higgins,
        She had four piggins,
And one flew over a sycamore tree.
        Poor Jane Higgins,
        She had three piggins,
And one was taken away for pork.
        Poor Jane Higgins,
        She had two piggins,
And one was sent to the Bishop of Cork.
        Poor Jane Higgins,
        She had one piggin,
And that was struck by a shower of hail,
        So poor Jane Higgins,
        She had no piggins,
And that's the end of my little pig tale.

James Reeves

Adventures of Isabel

Isabel met an enormous bear,
Isabel, Isabel, didn't care;
The bear was hungry, the bear was ravenous,
The bear's big mouth was cruel and cavernous.
The bear said, Isabel, glad to meet you,
How do, Isabel, now I'll eat you!
Isabel, Isabel, didn't worry,
Isabel didn't scream or scurry.
She washed her hands and she straightened her hair up,
Then Isabel quietly ate the bear up.

Once in a night as black as pitch
Isabel met a wicked old witch.
The witch's face was cross and wrinkled,
The witch's gums with teeth were sprinkled.
Ho ho, Isabel! the old witch crowed,
I'll turn you into an ugly toad!
Isabel, Isabel, didn't worry,
Isabel didn't scream or scurry,
She showed no rage and she showed no rancour,
But she turned the witch into milk and drank her.

Isabel met a hideous giant,
Isabel continued self-reliant.
The giant was hairy, the giant was horrid,
He had one eye in the middle of his forehead.
Good morning, Isabel, the giant said,
I'll grind your bones to make my bread.
Isabel, Isabel, didn't worry,
Isabel didn't scream or scurry.
She nibbled the zwieback that she always fed off,
And when it was gone, she cut the giant's head off.

Isabel met a troublesome doctor,
He punched and he poked till he really shocked her.
The doctor's talk was of coughs and chills
And the doctor's satchel bulged with pills.
The doctor said unto Isabel,
Swallow this, it will make you well.
Isabel, Isabel, didn't worry,
Isabel didn't scream or scurry.
She took those pills from the pill concocter,
And Isabel calmly cured the doctor.

Ogden Nash

Jonathan

Jonathan Gee
Went out with his cow
He climbed up a tree
And sat on a bough.
He sat on a bough
And it broke in half,
And John's old cow
Did nothing but laugh.

Rose Fyleman

The Lady and the Bear

A Lady came to a Bear by a Stream.
'O why are you fishing that way?
Tell me, dear Bear there by the Stream,
Why are you fishing that way?'

'I am what is known as a Biddly Bear, –
That's why I'm fishing this way.
We Biddlys are Pee-culiar Bears.
And so, – I'm fishing this way.

And besides, it seems there's a Law:
A most, most exactious Law
Says a Bear
Doesn't DARE
Use a Hook or a Line,
Or an old piece of Twine,
Not even the end of his Claw, Claw, Claw,
Not even the end of his Claw.
Yes, a Bear has to fish with his Paw, Paw, Paw.
A Bear has to fish with his Paw.'

'O it's wonderful how with a flick of your Wrist,
You can fish out a fish, out a fish, out a fish,
If *I* were a fish I just couldn't resist
You, when you are fishing that way, that way,
When you are fishing that way.'

And at that the Lady slipped from the Bank
And fell in the Stream still clutching a Rank,
But the Bear just sat there until she Sank;
And he went on fishing his way, his way,
And he went on fishing his way.

Theodore Roethke

Little Pippa

Pip Pip Pippety Pip
Slid on the lino
Slippety Slip
Fell downstairs
Trippety Trip
Tore her knickers
Rippety Rip
Started to cry
Drippety Drip
Poor little Pippa
Pippety Pip.

Spike Milligan

Here's a story

Here's a story
Of my friend Rory.
He fell off the wall –
And that's all!

Anon

Minnow Minnie

May I ask you if you've noticed,
May I ask you if you've seen
My minnow Minnie
Who was swimmin'
In your Ovaltine?
For you've gone and drunk it up, dear,
And she isn't in the cup, dear,
And she's nowhere to be found, dear.
Do you think that she has drowned, dear?

Shel Silverstein

It's dark in here

I am writing these lines
From inside a lion,
And it's rather dark in here.
So please excuse the handwriting
Which may not be too clear.
But this afternoon by the lion's cage
I'm afraid I got too near.
And I'm writing these lines
From inside a lion,
And it's rather dark in here.

Shel Silverstein

Riddle-me, riddle-me rumpty

Riddle-me, riddle-me rumpty,
There's a black cat on top of our plum-tree.
I'll bet you a crown
            that I'll fetch her down,
Riddle-me, riddle-me rumpty.

See here is a stone, and now it is thrown,
Riddle-me, riddle-me rumpty.
Oh it's just missed her head,
            smashed a window instead,
And the cat's still on top of our plum-tree.

Anon

An accident happened to my brother Jim

An accident happened to my brother Jim
When somebody threw a tomato at him –
Tomatoes are juicy and don't hurt the skin,
But this one was specially packed in a tin.

Anon

Milkman, milkman

Milkman, milkman, where have you been?
In buttermilk channel up to my chin.
I spilt my milk, and I spoilt my clothes,
And got a long icicle hung to my nose.

Anon

The three cooks

There were two cooks from Colebrook
And they fell out with our cook;
One was fat and one was thin,
They fought for the soup and all fell in.

Anon

Algy

Algy saw a bear;
The bear saw Algy.
The bear had a bulge;
The bulge was Algy.

Anon

A peanut sat on the railroad track

A peanut sat on the railroad track,
    His heart was all a-flutter;
Along came a train – the 9.15 –
    Toot, toot, peanut butter!

Anon

Little Sammy Soapsuds

When little Sammy Soapsuds
went out to take a ride,
on looking over London Bridge
he fell into the tide.

His parents never having taught
their little Sam to swim,
the tide soon got the mastery
and made an end of him.

Anon

Boa constrictor

Oh I'm being eaten by a boa constrictor,
A boa constrictor, a boa constrictor,
I'm being eaten by a boa constrictor,
And I don't like it . . . one bit!
Well what do you know . . . it's nibbling my toe,
Oh gee . . . it's up to my knee,
Oh my . . . it's up to my thigh,
Oh fiddle . . . it's up to my middle,
Oh heck . . . it's up to my neck,
Oh dread . . . it's . . . MMFFF.

Shel Silverstein

A sea-serpent saw a big tanker

A sea-serpent saw a big tanker,
Bit a hole in her side and then sank her.
    It swallowed the crew
    In a minute or two,
And then picked its teeth with the anchor.

Anon

Did you ever go fishing?

Did you ever go fishing on a bright sunny day –
Sit on a fence and have the fence give way?
Slide off the fence and rip your pants,
And see the little fishes do the hootchy-kootchy dance?

Anon

Mrs Poff

On the Mount of Bolliboff
Lived the tailor, Mr Poff.
One fine day his wife was sitting
On the balcony and knitting;
Down she fell – and Mrs Poff
Found her leg was broken off!
Came the doctor, and he said –
'Quick, a needle and some thread.'

When he'd stitched with might and main,
Mrs Poff could walk again.

*Translated from the German by
Rose Fyleman*

Inketty minketty monketty muddle

Inketty minketty monketty muddle,
the Lord Mayor of London
has stepped in a puddle

with his collar of gold
and his coat of red,
they've carried him home
and put him to bed.

Anon

Mrs Snipkin and Mrs Wobblechin

Skinny Mrs Snipkin,
With her little pipkin,
Sat by the fireside a-warming of her toes.
Fat Mrs Wobblechin,
With her little doublechin,
Sat by the window a-cooling of her nose.

Says this one to that one,
'Oh! you silly fat one,
Will you shut the window down? You're freezing me to
death!'

Says that one to t'other one,
'Good gracious, how you bother one!
There isn't air enough for me to draw my precious breath!'

Skinny Mrs Snipkin,
Took her little pipkin,
Threw it straight across the room as hard as she could throw;
Hit Mrs Wobblechin
On her little double chin,
And out of the window a-tumble she did go.

Laura Richards

Simple Simon

Simple Simon went a-fishing
For to catch a whale;
All the water he had got
Was in his mother's pail.

Simple Simon went a-skating
On a pond in June.
'Dear me,' he cried, 'this water's wet,
I fear I've come too soon!'

Simple Simon made a snowball,
And brought it home to roast;
He laid it down before the fire,
And soon the ball was lost.

Simple Simon bought a gun,
'To shoot a bird,' he said.
He held the gun the wrong way round,
And shot himself instead.

Anon

Bandy legs

As I was going to sell my eggs
I met a man with bandy legs,
Bandy legs and crooked toes;
I tripped up his heels, and he
     fell
       on
         his
           nose.

Anon

The hungry hunter

There was a hungry hunter
Went hunting for a hare,
But where he hoped the hare would be
He found a hairy bear!

He saw its eyes, he saw its claws,
He saw its teeth and then –
The hunter turned head-over-heels
And hurried home again.

Anon

There was an old man

There was an old man
Had a face made of cake,
He stuck it with currants
And put it to bake.

The oven was hot,
He baked it too much,
It came out covered
With crunchy crust.

The eyes went pop,
The currants went bang,
And that was the end
Of that old man.

James Kirkup

There's a hole in my bucket

There's a hole in my bucket, dear Conrad, dear Conrad.
  Then mend it, dear Freda, dear Freda, please do.
With what shall I mend it, dear Conrad, dear Conrad?
  With straw, my dear Freda, dear Freda, with straw.
But the straw is too long, dear Conrad, dear Conrad.
  Then trim it, dear Freda, dear Freda, please do.
But how shall I trim it, dear Conrad, dear Conrad?
  With a knife, my dear Freda, dear Freda, with a knife.
But the knife is too blunt, dear Conrad, dear Conrad.
  Then sharpen it, dear Freda, dear Freda, with a stone.
But the stone is too dry, dear Conrad, dear Conrad.
  Then wet it, dear Freda, dear Freda, please do.
But how shall I wet it, dear Conrad, dear Conrad?
  With water, dear Freda, dear Freda, with water.
How shall I fetch water, dear Conrad, dear Conrad?
  Use the bucket, dear Freda, dear Freda, please do.
There's a hole in my bucket, dear Conrad, dear Conrad.
  Then LEAVE IT, dear Freda, dear Freda, LEAVE IT.

German nursery rhyme

1

Animal fair

Froggy Boggy

Froggy Boggy
tried to jump
on a stone
and got a bump.

It made his eyes
wink and frown
and turned his nose
upside-down.

Anon

Our little dog

Our little dog
Is a terrible sinner –
He slinks up to the table
And tries to pinch the dinner.

Anon

Frog music

In a boggy old bog
by a loggy old log
sat a froggy old frog.

He had spots on his skin;
on his face was a grin
that was wide and was thin.

He was green. He was fat
as an old Cheshire cat.
He was flat where he sat.

While he hoped that a fly
would fly by by-and-by,

it was also his wish
to avoid Mr Fish,

Mr Turtle, and tall
Mr Heron, since all
of them *might* pay a call,

and just *might* be aware
of his grin, skin, and bare

bulgy head and those eyes,
very goggly in size.

So he grinned and just sat,
sat and sat, sat and sat,
looking silly like that.

But no fish saw him grin,
thinking, *Now* he'll jump in!

And no turtle a-cruise
thought him there in the ooze,

as a heron on one
leggy leg would have done.
Not a twitch in him – none.

Isn't life pretty grim
for a frog! Think of him.

But then think of that fly
flying by by-and-by.

David McCord

64

My donkey

My donkey, my dear,
Had a pain in his head;
A kind lady gave him
A bonnet of red,
And little shoes of lavender,
Lav- lav- lavender,
And little shoes of lavender
To keep him from the cold.

My donkey, my dear,
Had a pain in his throat;
A kind lady gave him
A button-up coat,
And little shoes of lavender,
Lav- lav- lavender,
And little shoes of lavender
To keep him from the cold.

My donkey, my dear,
Had a pain in his chest;
A kind lady gave him
A thick woolly vest,
And little shoes of lavender,
Lav- lav- lavender,
And little shoes of lavender,
To keep him from the cold.

*Translated from a French nursery
rhyme by Rose Fyleman*

Goosey, goosey gander

Goosey, goosey gander,
    Whither dost thou wander?
Upstairs, downstairs,
    And in my lady's chamber.
There I met an old man,
    And he had many cares –
For bad boys stole his apples,
    And birds pecked all his pears.

Anon

Five little squirrels

Five little squirrels sat up in a tree.
The first one said, 'What do I see?'
The second one said, 'A man with a gun.'
The third one said, 'Then we'd better run.'
The fourth one said, 'Let's hide in the shade.'
The fifth one said, 'I'm not afraid.'
Then BANG went the gun, and how they did run.

Anon

The lizard

A lizard wriggled on his belly
To Leeds to see his Aunty Nelly.
She said, 'What a long, long way you've come,
A-wriggling on your tired tum.'

Anon

Never say to a bat

Never say to a bat
'Hey, what are you at
Flying about all night?'
For if when you're sitting
That bat should come flitting,
You'll get a dreadful FRIGHT!

Barbara Ireson

Tiger

I'm a tiger
Striped with fur
Don't come near
Or I might Grrr
Don't come near
Or I might growl
Don't come near
Or I might
BITE!

Mary Ann Hoberman

The wolf couldn't catch me

The wolf couldn't catch me
For all his huff,
The wolf couldn't catch me
For all his puff,
The wolf couldn't catch me,
He's fit to bust,
He just couldn't see
My heels for dust.

Cynthia Mitchell

Min

I've got a dog
Whose name is Min,
As soon as she's out
She wants to come in.

She growls,
She howls,
She bumps,
She thumps,
She paws,
She claws,

And, finally, Min gets in.

Barbara Ireson

There was a little dog

There was a little dog and he had a little tail
And he used to wag, wag, wag it!
But when he was sad, because he'd been bad,
On the ground he would drag, drag, drag it!

Anon

The elephant carries a great big trunk

The elephant carries a great big trunk;
He never packs it with clothes;
It has no lock and it has no key,
But he takes it wherever he goes.

Anon

Lambs

Lambs are full of curly wool;
If they combed it, it would pull.
How lucky mother sheep don't care
If their children comb their hair.

Mary Ann Hoberman

Round the lake

As I was walking round the lake
I met a little rattlesnake,
I gave him so much ice-cream cake
It made his little belly-ache.

Anon

Who's that ringing at my door bell?

Who's that ringing at my door bell?
   A little pussy cat that isn't very well.
Rub its little nose with a little mutton fat,
   For that's the best cure for a little pussy cat.

Anon

Hello, Mr Python

Hello, Mr Python,
Curling round a tree,
Bet you'd like to make yourself
A dinner out of me.

Can't you change your habits
Crushing people's bones?
I wouldn't like a dinner
That emitted fearful groans.

Spike Milligan

Poor elephant

I'm sorry for old elephant,
He's not right in his skin.
It never seems to fit him,
Perhaps he is too thin.

His trunk is very heavy
And his big ears flippy flappy,
His skin sags all around him
And he does look so unhappy.

Barbara Ireson

A hamster by the name of Big Cheek

A hamster by the name of Big Cheek
Stored up nuts that would last for a week.
Alas, he ignored
That their being so stored
Made him look the most terrible freak.

Elizabeth Jennings

Our hamster

Our hamster's life:
there's not much
to it,
not much
to it.

He presses his pink nose
to the door of his cage
and decides for the fifty six
millionth time
that he can't get
through it.

Our hamster's life;
there's not much
to it,
not much
to it.

It's about the most boring
life in the world,
if he only
knew it.
He sleeps and he drinks and he eats.
He eats and he drinks and he sleeps.
He slinks and he dreeps.
He eats.

This process
he repeats.

Our hamster's life:
there's not much
to it,
not much
to it.

You'd think it would drive him bonkers,
going round and round on his wheel.
It's certainly driving me bonkers,

watching him
do it.

But he may be thinking:
That boy's life,
there's not much
to it,
not much
to it:

watching a hamster go round on a wheel.
It's driving me bonkers if he only knew it,

watching him
watching me
do it.'

Kit Wright

I had a little dog

I had a little dog, his name was Ball;
When I'd give him a little, he wanted it all.

I had a little dog, his name was Trot;
He held up his tail, all tied in a knot.

I had a little dog, his name was Blue;
When I took him on the road, he almost flew.

I had a little mule and his name was Jack;
I rode on his tail to save his back.

I had a little mule and his name was Jay;
I pulled his tail to hear him bray.

I had a little mule and he was very slick;
I pulled his tail to see him kick.

This little mule he kicked so high,
I thought that I would touch the sky.

I had a little mule, he was made of hay;
The first big wind that came blew him away.

Anon

Fuzzy Wuzzy

Fuzzy Wuzzy was a bear,
    A bear was Fuzzy Wuzzy.
When Fuzzy Wuzzy lost his hair
    He wasn't fuzzy, was he?

Anon

The Yak

There was a most odious Yak
Who took only toads on his Back:
If you asked for a Ride,
He would act very Snide,
And go humping off, yicketty-yak.

Theodore Roethke

The fly

Little fly upon the wall,
Have you got no clothes at all?
Have you got no shimmy shirt?
Have you got no petti-skirt?
Don't you ever brush your hair?
It's not because you've got no hair.
Is it because your mum don't care?

Poor fly!

Anon

An old grey horse stood on the wall

An old grey horse stood on the wall,
As daft as he was high.
He had no fear of falling down,
He thought he was a fly.

Anon

Dickery, dickery, dare

Dickery, dickery, dare,
The pig flew up in the air;
The man in brown soon brought him down,
Dickery, dickery, dare.

Anon

Ants live here

Ants live here
by the curb stone,
    see?
They worry a lot
about giants like me.

Lilian Moore

Daddy longlegs

Don't you think a daddy longlegs
has a lot of fun
using all those stilts to walk
and all those stilts to run?

Aileen Fisher

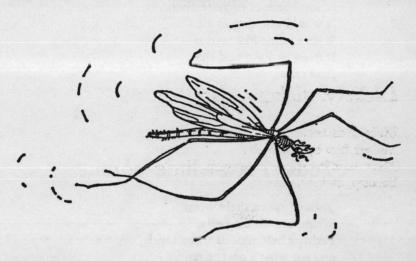

Snail's pace

Maybe it's so
that snails are slow.
They trudge along and tarry.

But isn't it true
you'd slow up, too,
if you had a house to carry?

Aileen Fisher

Worm

Worm
Is a term for a worm.
It sounds like a worm looks
Slow
Low to the ground
Usually brown
It would never have feathers
It would not sing at all
With a name like worm
It must be long and thin
And crawl.

Karla Kuskin

Today I saw a little worm

Today I saw a little worm,
Wriggling on his belly,
Perhaps he'd like to come inside,
and see what's on the telly.
Spike Milligan

Snakes

Snakes I can take or leave –
But when one comes near
I fear
I leave.

Barbara Ireson

Fancy that!

The outlaw

Into the house of a Mrs MacGruder
Came a very big outlaw
With a real six-shooter,
And he kicked the door
With his cowboy boot
And he searched the place
For valuable loot,
And he didn't take off his cowboy hat
But he quickly unlimbered his cowboy gat
And he cocked the gun
And he took his aim
And he called that Mrs MacG by name
And he said in a terrible outlaw drawl,
'Git me that cake . . . and git it all!'

And Mrs MacGruder patted his head,
'You may have a slice with some milk,' she said.

Felice Holman

Five tiny green peas

Five tiny green peas lying in a row
Inside a small green pod, one day began to grow.
They grew and they grew and they didn't stop
Until one day their pod went POP!

Anon

Pinch me, Punch me and Tread-on-my-toes

Pinch me, Punch me and Tread-on-my-toes
Went down to the river to bathe.
Two of the three were drowned.
Who do you think was saved?

Anon

What'll we do?

What'll we do?
The frog's got 'flu.
Lie him down
In a dressing gown,
Wrap him up
And give him a sup,
Give him a pill
To make him well,
Give him a poke
To make him croak.
Oh dear! What'll we do?
Poor old froggie,
He's got 'flu.

*Translated from the German
by Brian Alderson*

I once saw an ant as big as a mouse

I once saw an ant as big as a mouse,
Running and scratching about my house;
I once saw a mouse as big as a cat,
That mewed and chewed inside an old hat;
I once saw a cat as big as a pig,
That ate an old apple, three pears and a fig;
I once saw a pig as big as a cow,
That knew how to curtsey but not how to bow;
I once saw a cow as big as a whale,
That never gave milk, but only brown ale;
I once saw a whale, I once saw a whale . . .
Nothing is bigger, and so ends my tale.

John Cunliffe

One day a boy went walking

One day a boy went walking
    And walked into a store,
He bought a pound of sausages
    And laid them on the floor.
The boy began to whistle,
    He whistled up a tune,
And all the little sausages
    Danced around the room.

Anon

The Land of the Bumbley Boo

In the land of the Bumbley Boo
The people are red, white and blue,
They never blow noses,
Or ever wear closes;
What a sensible thing to do!

In the land of the Bumbley Boo
You can buy Lemon pie at the Zoo;
They give away Foxes
In little Pink Boxes
And Bottles of Dandelion Stew.

In the land of the Bumbley Boo
You never see a Gnu,
But thousands of cats
Wearing trousers and hats
Made of Pumpkins and Pelican Glue!

Oh, the Bumbley Boo! the Bumbley Boo!
That's the place for me and you!
So hurry! Let's run!
The train leaves at one!
For the land of the Bumbley Boo!
The wonderful Bumbley Boo-Boo-Boo!
The Wonderful Bumbley BOO!!!

                    Spike Milligan

There were three ghostesses

There were three ghostesses
Sitting on postesses
Eating buttered toastesses
And greasing their fistesses
Right up to their wristesses.
Weren't they beastesses
To make such feastesses!

Anon

Once there was a creepy-crawly

Once there was a creepy-crawly
Climbing up the castle wall-y,
Weather changed to stormy-squally
And the rain began to fall-y;
Down from the castle wall-y
Tumbled little creepy-crawly.

Flump!

*Translated from the German
by Brian Alderson*

84

Said the monkey to the donkey

Said the monkey to the donkey,
'What'll you have to drink?'
Said the donkey to the monkey,
'I'd like a swig of ink.'

Anon

Toeses

Moses supposes
his toeses are roses
but Moses supposes
erroneously.
For nobody's toeses
are posies of roses
as Moses supposes
his toeses to be.

Anon

Nicholas Ned

Nicholas Ned,
He lost his head,
And put a turnip on instead;
But then, ah, me!
He could not see,
So he thought it was night, and he went to bed.

Laura Richards

The telephone and the door-bell

Ring, ring, ring . . .

'Door-bell, your noise I cannot stand,'
Called the telephone from the hall.

DRING, dring, dring . . .

'Your shrill,' cried out the front door-bell,
Just drives me up the wall.'

'I'll drown your ring!'

'I'll drown your dring!'

RING, DRING, RING, DRING, RING, DRING . . .

Barbara Ireson

Michael Finnegan

There was an old man named Michael Finnegan,
He grew a long beard right on his chinnigan,
Along came a wind and blew it in again –
Poor old Michael Finnegan.

Anon

Up in the North

Up in the North, a long way off,
The donkey's got the whooping-cough.

Anon

The elephant

The elephant is a graceful bird;
   It flits from twig to twig.
It builds its nest in a rhubarb tree
   And whistles like a pig.

Anon

The tickle rhyme

'Who's that tickling my back?' said the wall.
'Me,' said a small
caterpillar. 'I'm learning
to crawl.'

Ian Serraillier

A mouse in her room

A mouse in her room woke Miss Dowd.
She was frightened and screamed very loud.
Then a happy thought hit her —
To scare off the critter
She sat up in bed and meowed.

Anon

The pot calling the kettle black

'Bubble!' said the pot
To the dancing kettle
(Who was in fine fettle)
'You are black as soot!'

'Pouff!' said the kettle
To the jiggety pot
(Who was feeling hot)
'You are black as a beetle!'

'Bubble, ubble, ubble,'
Said the pot in wrath
With his voice full of broth
'I will get you into trouble.'

'Fiddle, diddle, diddle,'
Said the kettle in a rage
(He was old for his age)
'You have soup down your middle!'

'Fuss, fuss, fuss,'
Hissed the pot on the fire
Boiling higher and higher,
'You're spitting like the puss!'

'I'll make you behave,'
Said the kettle from above
As he spat from the stove
'You're a rogue and a knave!'

'Bother, bother, bother,'
Said the cook running in,
'What a fuss, what a din,
You're as black as each other!'

Pauline Clarke

The ostrich is a silly bird

The ostrich is a silly bird,
With scarcely any mind.
He often runs so very fast,
He leaves himself behind.

And when he gets there has to stand
And hang about till night,
Without a blessed thing to do
Until he comes in sight.

Mary E. Wilkins Freeman

Peter and Michael

Peter and Michael were two little menikin,
They kept a cock and a fat little henikin;
Instead of an egg, it laid a gold penikin,
Oh, how they wish it would do it againikin!

Anon

Dogs can't talk

'Dogs can't talk,' I told my puppy.
'Oh, yes, they can', he said,
So my puppy was told
That at just six weeks old
He was much too young to know.

Barbara Ireson

Homes for rent

If only the rabbits
Would give up their habits
Of living underground,
The moles and voles
Could have their holes,
And there would be more
To go round.

Barbara Ireson

Lumps

Humps are lumps
and so are mumps.

Bumps make lumps
on heads.

Mushrooms grow
in clumps of lumps –
on clumps of stumps,
in woods and dumps.

Springs spring lumps
in beds.

Mosquito bites
make itchy lumps.

Frogs on logs
make twitchy lumps.

Judith Thurman

Beds have legs

Beds have legs, but cannot walk,
Cups have lips, but cannot talk,
Cars have boots that cannot kick,
Boots have tongues that cannot lick.

Barbara Ireson

A rabbit raced a turtle

A rabbit raced a turtle,
You know the turtle won;
And Mister Bunny came in late –
A little hot cross bun.

Anon

Momotara

Where did Momotara go,
With a hoity-toity-tighty?
He went to lay the giants low,
The wicked ones and mighty.

What did Momotara take?
His monkey, dog and pheasant,
Some dumplings and an almond cake,
Which made the journey pleasant.

How did Momotara fare
Upon the fearful meeting?
He seized the giants by the hair
And gave them all a beating.

What did Momotara bring?
Oh, more than you could measure:
A silver coat, a golden ring
And a waggon-load of treasure.

What did Momotara do?
He sat himself astride it;
The monkey pushed, the pheasant drew
And the little dog ran beside it.

*Translated from the Japanese
by Rose Fyleman*

The alligator

The alligator chased his tail
Which hit him on the snout;
He nibbled, gobbled, swallowed it,
And turned right inside-out.

Mary Macdonald

A frog and a flea

A frog and a flea
And a kangaroo
Once jumped for a prize
In a pot of glue;
The kangaroo stuck
And so did the flea,
And the frog limped home
With a fractured knee.

Cynthia Mitchell

Well I never

Well I never, did you ever
See a monkey dressed in leather?
Leather eyes, leather nose,
Leather breeches to his toes.

Anon

What they said

It's four o'clock,
Said the cock.

It's still dark,
Said the lark.

What's that?
Said the cat.

I want to sleep,
Said the sheep.

A bad habit,
Said the rabbit.

Of course,
Said the horse.

Let's have a spree,
Said the bee.

But where?
Said the hare.

In the barrow,
Said the sparrow.

I'm too big,
Said the pig.

In the house,
said the mouse.

But the dog said – Bow-wow,
It's too late now.

*Translated from a German nursery rhyme
by Rose Fyleman*

Three young rats

Three young rats with black felt hats,
   Three young ducks with white straw flats,
      Three young dogs with curling tails,
         Three young cats with demi-veils,
            Went out to walk with two young pigs
            In satin vests and sorrel wigs;
               But suddenly it chanced to rain,
               And so they all went home again.

Anon

Hicketty picketty

Hicketty picketty, pizer jiggitty,
Pompalorum jig:
Every man that has no hair
He ought to wear a wig.
A sixpenny bit on the tuppenny railway,
Half a crown on the rollicking sea,
And nothing at all on the hurdy-gurdy –
That's the one for me!

Anon

Hinx, minx

Hinx, minx, the old Witch winks,
The fat begins to fry;
There's no one at home but Jumping Joan,
The old black cat, and I.

Hinx, minx, the old Witch winks,
The fish jump out of the pan;
Jumping Joan is off to the moon
As fast as ever she can.

Anon

Me, myself and I

My body

Wherever I go, it also goes,
And when it's dressed, I'm wearing clothes.

William Jay Smith

In my new clothing

In my new clothing
    I feel so different
    I must
Look like someone else.

Japanese poem by Bashō, translated by
Harold G. Henderson

Sometimes

Sometimes
when I skip or hop
or when I'm
       jumping

Suddenly
I like to stop
and listen to me
       thumping.

Lilian Moore

Sing-song

This is a song
I like to sing,
Boodley, boodley, boo.
And if you like
I'll sing it to you,
Boodley, boodley, boo.

I sing it high,
I sing it low,
I sing it everywhere I go.
I sing in shops
And in the park,
I sing it sitting in the dark.
I sing it fast,
I sing it slow,
I sing it every way I know,
And when it's time
To go to bed,
I sing it standing on my head.

Boodley, boodley, boo.

Barbara Ireson

I wish I were a little grub

I wish I were a little grub
With whiskers round my tummy.
I'd climb into a honey pot
And make my tummy gummy.

Anon

99

A farmyard song

I had a cat and my cat pleased me,
I fed my cat by the old oak tree.
    Cat went fiddle-i-fee.

I had a hen and my hen pleased me,
I fed my hen by the old oak tree.
    Hen went chimmy-chuck, chimmy-chuck,
    Cat went fiddle-i-fee.

I had a duck and my duck pleased me,
I fed my duck by the old oak tree.
    Duck went quack-quack, quack-quack,
    Hen went chimmy-chuck, chimmy-chuck,
    Cat went fiddle-i-fee.

I had a goose and my goose pleased me,
I fed my goose by the old oak tree.
    Goose went swishy-swashy, swishy-swashy,
    Duck went quack-quack, quack-quack,
    Hen went chimmy-chuck, chimmy-chuck,
    Cat went fiddle-i-fee.

I had a sheep and my sheep pleased me,
I fed my sheep by the old oak tree.
   Sheep went baa-baa, baa-baa,
   Goose went swishy-swashy, swishy-swashy,
   Duck went quack-quack, quack-quack,
   Hen went chimmy-chuck, chimmy-chuck,
   Cat went fiddle-i-fee.

I had a pig and my pig pleased me,
I fed my pig by the old oak tree.
   Pig went griffy-gruffy, griffy-gruffy,
   Sheep went baa-baa, baa-baa,
   Goose went swishy-swashy, swishy-swashy,
   Duck went quack-quack, quack-quack,
   Hen went chimmy-chuck, chimmy-chuck,
   Cat went fiddle-i-fee.

I had a cow and my cow pleased me,
I fed my cow by the old oak tree.
   Cow went moo-moo, moo-moo,
   Pig went griffy-gruffy, griffy-gruffy,
   Sheep went baa-baa, baa-baa,
   Goose went swishy-swashy, swishy-swashy,
   Duck went quack-quack, quack-quack,
   Hen went chimmy-chuck, chimmy-chuck,
   Cat went fiddle-i-fee.

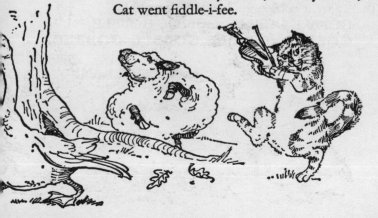

I had a horse and my horse pleased me,
I fed my horse by the old oak tree.
    Horse went neigh-neigh, neigh-neigh,
    Cow went moo-moo, moo-moo,
    Pig went griffy-gruffy, griffy-gruffy,
    Sheep went baa-baa, baa-baa,
    Goose went swishy-swashy, swishy-swashy,
    Duck went quack-quack, quack-quack,
    Hen went chimmy-chuck, chimmy-chuck,
    Cat went fiddle-i-fee.

I had a dog and my dog pleased me,
I fed my dog by the old oak tree.
    Dog went bow-wow, bow-wow,
    Horse went neigh-neigh, neigh-neigh,
    Cow went moo-moo, moo-moo,
    Pig went griffy-gruffy, griffy-gruffy,
    Sheep went baa-baa, baa-baa,
    Goose went swishy-swashy, swishy-swashy,
    Duck went quack-quack, quack-quack,
    Hen went chimmy-chuck, chimmy-chuck,
    Cat went fiddle-i-fee.

I had a turkey and my turkey pleased me,
I fed my turkey by the old oak tree.
    Turkey went gobble-gobble, gobble-gobble
      GOBBLE-GOBBLE, GOBBLE-GOBBLE,
      GOBBLE-GOBBLE, GOBBLE-GOBBLE...

            AND OFF I RAN!

              Anon

Whenever there's snow

Whenever there's snow
I rush out and go
Into the street
So that my feet
Go SLISH, SLOSH,
   SLISH, SLOSH.

When snow turns to rain
I rush out again
Into the street
So that my feet
Go SPLISH, SPLOSH,
   SPLISH, SPLOSH.

Barbara Ireson

New shoes

My shoes are new and squeaky shoes,
They're very shiny, creaky shoes,
I wish I had my leaky shoes
That Mother threw away.

I liked my old brown leaky shoes
Much better than these creaky shoes,
These shiny, creaky, squeaky shoes
I've got to wear today.

Anon

103

In the park

I went to the park today
and saw these things on the way –

Saw a dog chase a hog
off a log

Saw a cat in a hat
on a mat

Saw a cow and a sow
take a bow

Saw a hen fill a pen
full of men

Saw a crow with a bow
flying low

Saw a bear and a mare
climb a stair

Saw a rat push a bat
in the fat

Saw an ox wearing socks
chase a fox

Saw a mole try to roll
down a pole

Saw a pig in a wig
dance a jig.

And if you want to see them too
Just come along at half-past zoo.

Barbara Ireson

Yes

Yes
Yes
I like yes
I like it when I ask for things
And when you say yes
Yes
Yes
Let's take a walk
Let's bake a cake
Let's sing a song
Yes
Yes
And yet sometimes
I don't like yes
Like when you say
You've made a mess
Please clean it up
Or
Time for bed
Or
Time to go
And then I guess
That I like yes
A little less
Yes?
Yes.

Mary Ann Hoberman

The indignant male

The way they scrub
Me in the tub,
I think there's
    Hardly
    Any
      Doubt
Sometime they'll rub
And rub and rub
Until they simply
    Rub
    Me
    Out.

A. B. Ross

Pins and needles

O dear, o dear,
I sat on my feet
Under the trees
With an apple to eat,
I sat on my feet
Till they went to sleep,
I sat on my feet
In an awkward heap,
And when I stood up
My feet were not there!
I wanted to walk,
But they did not care,
And thousands and thousands
Of pointed pins
Prickle and popple
Into my shins:
And millions and millions
Of needley points
Nibble and wobble
Into my joints:
And needles and pins
Bending in half
Make me jump
And make me laugh!

O dear, o dear,
Do take care
Of the needles and pins
Which come from nowhere,
And mind how you sit
Under dappled trees
Eating an apple
With doubled-up knees.

Pauline Clarke

Furry bear

If I were a bear
    And a big bear too,
I shouldn't much care
    If it froze or snew;
I shouldn't much mind
    If it snowed or friz –
I'd be all fur-lined
    With a coat like his!

For I'd have fur boots and a brown fur wrap,
And brown fur knickers and a big fur cap.
I'd have a fur muffle-ruff to cover my jaws,
And brown fur mittens on my big brown paws.
With a big brown furry-down up to my head,
I'd sleep all winter in a big fur bed.

A. A. Milne

If I were a fish

Splash, splosh!
Whenever I wash
I wish and wish and wish
That I lived in the water all day long
Like a slithery, slippery fish.

Splash, splish!
If I were a fish
I wouldn't have to wash.
I wouldn't need soap or a towel or a sponge,
But I'd splish –
        And I'd splash –
            And I'd splosh!

Alison Winn

Fair exchange

I'll give a candle
or a spangle
or a bangle
or a nice shiny handle
or some rolled-up string.

I'll give a buckle
or a pickle
or a nickel
or a sprig of honeysuckle
or a copper ring . . .

If you will only let me see
Your swelled-up hornet sting.

Aileen Fisher

When I went out for a walk one day

When I went out for a walk one day,
    My head fell off and rolled away,
And when I saw that it was gone –
    I picked it up and put it on.

When I went into the street
    Someone shouted, 'Look at your feet!'
I looked at them and sadly said,
    'I've left them both asleep in bed!'

Anon

Which

Would you rather be
Thin
as
a
Pin
or
Lean
as
a
Sardine?
Or do you agree
It would be better if you were as Thick as an old oak Tree,
Fat as a pig, or harvest pumpkin, or dusty honey bee?

O dear me, no
I don't want to become
Tiny like Tom Thumb
or grow
Small enough to live with a mouse
in his house;

I don't want to be as Big as an elephant, Wider than a bus,
Huge as a fairy tale giant or a hippopotamus,
I think I'd rather stay
Just as I am if I may,
The same size tomorrow as yesterday

Leonard Clark

Afraid of the dark

I'm Reginald Clark. I'm afraid of the dark
So I always insist on the light on,
And my teddy to hug,
And my blanket to rub,
And my thumby to suck or to bite on,
And three bedtime stories,
Two trips to the toilet,
Two prayers, and five hugs from my mommy,
I'm Reginald Clark, I'm afraid of the dark
So please do not close this book on me.

Shel Silverstein

I do not wish I were a cat

I do not wish I were a cat
With fine black whiskers
Smoky fur.
I do not want a tail and paws
I only wish that I could purr.

Karla Kuskin

Yum, yum!

A – apple pie

Little Pollie Pillikins
Peeped into the kitchen,
'H'm,' says she, 'Ho,' says she,
    'Nobody there!'
Only little meeny mice,
Miniken and miching
On the big broad flagstones, empty and bare.

Greedy Pollie Pillikins
Crept into the pantry,
There stood an Apple Pasty,
    Sugar white as snow.
Off the shelf she toppled it,
Quick and quiet and canty,
And the meeny mice they watched her
    On her tip-tap-toe.

'Thief, Pollie Pillikins!'
Crouching in the shadows there,
Flickering in the candle-shining,
    Foo, fo, fum!
Munching up the pastry,
Crunching up the apples,
'Thief!' squeaked the smallest mouse,
    'Pollie, spare a crumb!'

Walter de la Mare

The toaster

A silver-scaled Dragon with jaws flaming red
Sits at my elbow and toasts my bread.
I hand him fat slices, and then, one by one,
He hands them back when he sees they are done.

William Jay Smith

The King's breakfast

The King asked
The Queen, and
The Queen asked
The Dairymaid:
'Could we have some butter for
The Royal slice of bread?'
The Queen asked
The Dairymaid,
The Dairymaid
Said, 'Certainly,
I'll go and tell
The cow
Now
Before she goes to bed.'

The Dairymaid
She curtsied,
And went and told
The Alderney:
'Don't forget the butter for
The Royal slice of bread.'
The Alderney
Said sleepily:
'You'd better tell
His Majesty
That many people nowadays
Like marmalade
Instead.'

The Dairymaid
Said, 'Fancy!'
And went to
Her Majesty.
She curtsied to the Queen, and
She turned a little red:
'Excuse me,
Your Majesty,
For taking of
The liberty,
But marmalade is tasty, if
It's very
Thickly
Spread.'

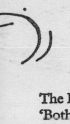

The Queen said
'Oh!'
And went to
His Majesty:
'Talking of the butter for
The Royal slice of bread,
Many people
Think that
Marmalade
Is nicer.
Would you like to try a little
Marmalade
Instead?'

The King said,
'Bother!'
And then he said,
'Oh deary me!'
The king sobbed, 'Oh,
    deary me!'
And went back to bed.
'Nobody,'
He whimpered,
'Could call me
A fussy man;
I *only* want
A little bit
Of butter for
My bread!'

The Queen said,
'There, there!'
And went to
The Dairymaid.
The Dairymaid
Said 'There, there!'
And went to the shed.
The cow said,
'There, there!
I didn't really
Mean it;
Here's milk for his porringer
And butter for his bread.'

The Queen took
The butter
And brought it to
His Majesty;
The King said,
'Butter, eh?'
And bounced out of bed.
'Nobody,' he said,
As he kissed her
Tenderly,
'Nobody,' he said,
As he slid down
The banisters,
'Nobody,
My darling,
Could call me
A fussy man –
BUT
I do like a little bit of butter to my bread!'

A. A. Milne

My toaster

'Here, brown these,'
I tell my toaster
When I come down at eight.
He glows with pride
And toasts both sides,
Then chucks them on my plate.

Barbara Ireson

There was a king

There was a king who had four sons,
For breakfast they had currant buns,
It seems a funny thing to me,
But every day they each ate three.
Every day the baker came,
Every day it was the same,
Every day at half past eight
He left twelve buns at the castle gate.

Anon

Pillykin, Willykin Winkey Wee

Oh, Pillykin, Willykin Winkey Wee!
How does the president take his tea?
He takes it with melons, he takes it with milk,
He takes it with syrup and sassafras silk;
He takes it without, he takes it within,
Oh, Punky-doodle and Jollapin!

Anon

Through the teeth

Through the teeth
And past the gums.
Look out, stomach,
Here it comes!

Anon

The old man of Peru

There was an old man of Peru,
Who dreamt he was eating his shoe.
  He woke in the night
  In a terrible fright,
And found it was perfectly true.

Anon

I'm just going out for a moment

I'm just going out for a moment.

Why?

To make a cup of tea.

Why?

Because I'm thirsty.

Why?

Because it's hot.

Why?

Because the sun's shining.

Why?

Because it's summer.

Why?

Because that's when it is.

Why?

Why don't you stop saying why?

Why?

Mike Rosen

Railway navvy

I'm a navvy, you're a navvy,
Working on the line.
Five-and-twenty bob a week
And all the overtime.
Roast beef, boiled beef,
Puddings made of eggs –
Up jumps a navvy
With a pair of sausage legs!

Anon

Tip-top

Tip-top tip-top
tap a speckled egg.
Once to put him in his cup
and twice to crack his head.

Michael Rosen

Sleeping sardines

'I'm tired of eating just beans,' says I,
So I opened a can of sardines.
But they started to squeak,
'Hey, we're tryin' to sleep.
We were snuggled up tight
Till you let in the light.
You big silly sap, let us finish our nap.
So close up the lid!'
So that's what I did . . .
Will somebody please pass the beans?

Shel Silverstein

Halloweena Hecatee

Halloweena Hecatee
Couldn't make a cup of tea!
The only potion she can brew
Is wishy-washy mousetail stew;
Flying bezoms don't scare me,
Halloweena Hecatee.

Cynthia Mitchell

Jeremiah Obadiah

Jeremiah Obadiah, puff, puff, puff,
When he gives his messages, he snuffs, snuffs, snuffs,
When he goes to school by day, he roars, roars, roars,
When he goes to bed at night, he snores, snores, snores,
When he goes to Christmas treat, he eats plum-duff,
Jeremiah Obadiah, puff, puff, puff.

Anon

John Bull

John Bull, John Bull,
Your belly's so full
You can't jump over
A three-legged stool.

Anon

What's in the cupboard?

What's in the cupboard?
Says Mr Hubbard.
A knuckle of veal,
Says Mr Beal.
Is that all?
Says Mr Ball.
And enough too,
Says Mr Glue –

And away they all flew.

Anon

Jolly Roger

Jolly Roger lived up a tree.
You climbed there by a rope.
I'd often go for a cup of tea,
Which he brewed up with soap.

Once I found a sock in mine.
It made me wince a bit,
But Roger told me, 'Never mind,
It's old and doesn't fit.'

Anon

Pepper and salt

I peppered my fish and salted my chips
At supper the other night,
Then all of a sudden my fish gave a sneeze
And I got a terrible fright!

Barbara Ireson

Alligator

From Sydney Zoo
An Alligator
Was put on board
A flying freighter.
He ate the pilot
AND the navigator
Then asked for more,
With mashed potater.

Spike Milligan

Robert Rowley

Robert Rowley rolled a round roll round,
A round roll Robert Rowley rolled round;
Where rolled the round roll
Robert Rowley rolled round?

Anon

Malice at Buckingham Palace

Outside Buckingham Palace
  a dog was barking one day
When out of a house
  came a chocolate mouse
And frightened that doggie away.

And so that chocolate mousie
  was taken to the Queen –
Who swallowed him up gobbledy slup
  with a gobbledy slup.
I do think that was mean.

Spike Milligan

Jam

'Spread,' said Toast to Butter,
And Butter spread.
'That's better, Butter,'
Toast said.

'Jam,' said Butter to Toast.
'Where are you, Jam,
When we need you most?'
Jam: 'Here I am,

Strawberry, trickly and sweet.
How are you, Spoon?'
'I'm helping somebody eat,
I think, pretty soon.'

David McCord

The diner at Crewe

A diner while dining at Crewe
Found quite a large mouse in his stew.
  Said the waiter, 'Don't shout
  And wave it about,
Or the rest will be wanting one, too!'

Anon

Peas for breakfast

peas for breakfast please he said
and a plateful of peas is what he got

and when he went to bed last night
I heard him say: more peas please

you know, I don't think he eats much else
one full bowl three times a day

it would fill a room all those peas you know
but I think
even if he had to wade up to his knees in peas
he would still come here saying: more peas please.

Mike Rosen

The Old Person

There was an Old Person whose habits
  Induced him to feed upon rabbits;
      When he'd eaten eighteen,
      He turned perfectly green,
Upon which he relinquished those habits.

Edward Lear

Exploding gravy

My mother's big green gravy boat
Once thought he was a navy boat.

I poured him over my mashed potatoes
And out swam seven swift torpedoes.

Torpedoes whizzed and whirred, and – WHAM!
One bumped smack into my hunk of ham

And blew up with an awful roar,
Flinging my carrots on the floor.

Exploding gravy! That's so silly!
Now all I ever eat is chili.

X. J. Kennedy

Pete's sweets

Pete
will eat
anything
if it's sweet.

Peppermint soup,
or ice cream on toast.

Though what he likes most
is a jelly sandwich
without any bread.

Or instead,
a bubble-gum chop.
Chew your meat thoroughly, Pete.
   'I am. Cancha hear me?' Pop!

Eve Merriam

If all the hills were butter

If all the hills were butter
And all the valleys groats –
Then out would come the hot, hot sun,
The butter-mountains all would run
And we'd have porridge by the ton!

Translated from the German by
Brian Alderson

Miss T.

It's a very odd thing –
　　As odd as can be –
That whatever Miss T. eats
　　Turns into Miss T.;
Porridge and apples,
　　Mince, muffins and mutton,
Jam, junket, jumbles –
　　Not a rap, not a button
It matters; the moment
　　They're out of her plate,
Though shared by Miss Butcher
　　And sour Mr Bate;
Tiny and cheerful,
　　And neat as can be,
Whatever Miss T. eats
　　Turns into Miss T.

Walter de la Mare

Have you ever?

Have you ever spread jam on ham?
Have you ever put spice on rice?
Have you ever taken
Pink ice cream with bacon –

You'll find that they're ever so nice!

Barbara Ireson

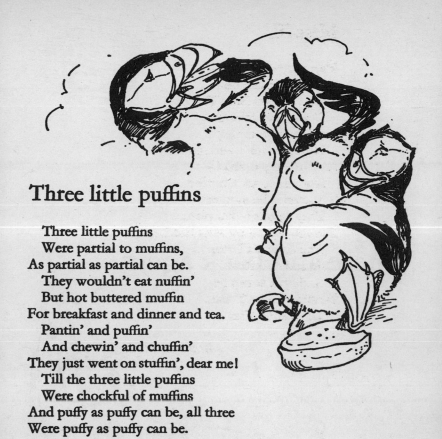

Three little puffins

Three little puffins
Were partial to muffins,
As partial as partial can be.
They wouldn't eat nuffin'
But hot buttered muffin
For breakfast and dinner and tea.
Pantin' and puffin'
And chewin' and chuffin'
They just went on stuffin', dear me!
Till the three little puffins
Were chockful of muffins
And puffy as puffy can be, all three
Were puffy as puffy can be.

Eleanor Farjeon

I eat my peas with honey

I eat my peas with honey.
I've done it all my life.
It makes the peas taste funny
But it keeps 'em on the knife!

Anon

There and back again

Mr Green's story

Mr Mauve walked out one day
And went to call on Mr Grey.
Mr Grey said, 'Perhaps we might
Go and see our dear friend White.'
But White was out and in the town
They bumped into Mr Brown.
Mr Brown said White and Black
Had gone away and not come back.
'The only thing for you to do,'
He said, 'is visit Mr Blue.'
And so they went, so I've been told,
And that's how they ran into Gold.

I heard all this from Mr Green,
And that's the last time they were seen.

Barbara Ireson

The Old Person of Ickley

There was an Old Person of Ickley,
Who could not abide to ride quickly;
  He rode to Karnack
  On a tortoise's back,
That moony Old Person of Ickley.

Edward Lear

The Old Person of Ware

There was an Old Person of Ware,
Who rode on the back of a Bear;
  When they ask'd, 'Does it trot?'
  He said: 'Certainly not!
He's a Moppsikon Floppsikon Bear!'

Edward Lear

Poppleton to Pippleton

The people of Poppleton
Are on their way to Pippleton
To see their friends today.
And when they get to Pippleton,
They'll all go home to Poppleton
And this is what they'll say –

The people of Pippleton
Are on their way to Poppleton
To see their friends today.
And when they get to Poppleton,
They'll all go home to Pippleton
And this is what they'll say –

The people of Poppleton
Are on their way to Pippleton
To see their friends today.
And when they get to Pippleton,
They'll all go home to Poppleton
And this is what they'll say . . .

Barbara Ireson

Twiddle-di-dee, twiddle-di-dee

Twiddle-di-dee, twiddle-di-dee,
I went for a walk with a bumble bee,
Past the farm and the linden tree;
Buzz, buzz, twiddle-di-dee!

Twiddle-di-dake, twiddle-di-dake,
I went for a walk with a slithery snake,
Through the wood and past the lake;
Hiss, hiss, twiddle-di-dake.

Traditional

The Old Person of Wilts

There was an Old Person of Wilts,
Who constantly walked upon Stilts;
   He wreathed them with lilies
    And daffy-down-dillies,
That elegant Person of Wilts.

Edward Lear

The rocket that flew to the moon

Here is a rocket that flew to the moon.

Here is a man, Professor McSpoon,
Who constructed the rocket that flew to the moon.

Here is Billy, who asked for a ride
In the moonrocket. 'Certainly, come inside,'
Said the clever inventor, Professor McSpoon,
Who constructed the rocket that flew to the moon.

Here goes the blast-off, buzzing and fizzing,
As into the sky the rocket goes whizzing
With Billy, the boy who asked for a ride
In the moonrocket, crouching and clinging inside,
With the clever inventor, Professor McSpoon,
Who constructed the rocket that flew to the moon.

Here is the moon, placid and white,
Shining peacefully down that night,
When the blast-off went banging and buzzing and fizzing,
As into the sky the rocket went whizzing,
With Billy, the boy who asked for a ride
In the moonrocket, crouching and clinging inside,
With the clever inventor, Professor McSpoon,
Who constructed the rocket that flew to the moon.

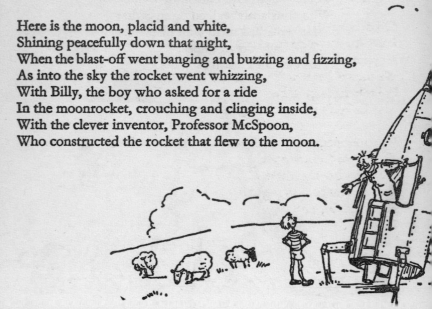

Here is the rocket, in orbit, then landing,
The Professor and Billy climb out and are standing
At last on the moon, which, placid and white,
Was shining peacefully down that night
When the blast-off went banging and buzzing and fizzing,
As into the sky the rocket went whizzing
With Billy, the boy who asked for a ride
In the moonrocket, crouching and clinging inside
With the clever inventor, Professor McSpoon,
Who constructed the rocket that flew to the moon.

Wilma Horsbrugh

Hoppity

Christopher Robin goes
Hoppity, hoppity,
Hoppity, hoppity, hop.
Whenever I tell him
Politely to stop it, he
Says he can't possibly stop.

If he stopped hopping, he couldn't go anywhere,
Poor little Christopher
Couldn't go anywhere . . .
That's why he *always* goes
Hoppity, hoppity,
Hoppity,
Hoppity,
Hop.

A. A. Milne

I went downtown

I went downtown
To see Mrs Brown.
She gave me a nickel
To buy a pickle.
The pickle was sour,
She gave me a flower.
The flower was dead,
She gave me a thread.
The thread was thin,
She gave me a pin.
The pin was sharp,
She gave me a harp.
The harp began to sing
Minnie and a minnie and a ha ha ha.

Anon

Chuffa-luffa steam train

Chuffa-luffa steam train,
Chuggle up the track,
Chuggle up to Nowhere,
Chuggle-chuffle back.

Ever been to Nowhere?
No – what's there?
Nothing.
Nothing?
Nothing but a steam train,
Chuggle up the track,
Chuggle up to Nowhere,
Chuggle-chuffle back.

Peter Wesley-Smith

To market ride the gentlemen

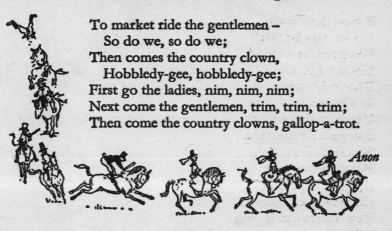

To market ride the gentlemen –
    So do we, so do we;
Then comes the country clown,
    Hobbledy-gee, hobbledy-gee;
First go the ladies, nim, nim, nim;
Next come the gentlemen, trim, trim, trim;
Then come the country clowns, gallop-a-trot.

Anon

At the seaside

I went to the sea and what did I see?
            Ten sharks,
            Nine seals,
            Eight eels,
            Seven crabs,
            Six prawns,
            Five shrimps,
            Four clams,
            Three whelks,
            Two worms –
And when I was leaving at half past three
And taking them back to eat them for tea,
One great big whale came after me,
When I went to see the sea.

Barbara Ireson

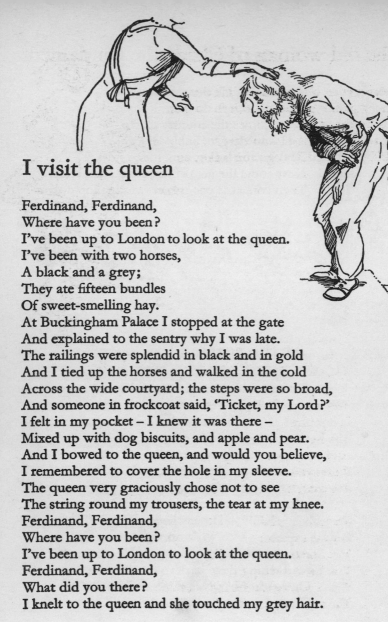

I visit the queen

Ferdinand, Ferdinand,
Where have you been?
I've been up to London to look at the queen.
I've been with two horses,
A black and a grey;
They ate fifteen bundles
Of sweet-smelling hay.
At Buckingham Palace I stopped at the gate
And explained to the sentry why I was late.
The railings were splendid in black and in gold
And I tied up the horses and walked in the cold
Across the wide courtyard; the steps were so broad,
And someone in frockcoat said, 'Ticket, my Lord?'
I felt in my pocket – I knew it was there –
Mixed up with dog biscuits, and apple and pear.
And I bowed to the queen, and would you believe,
I remembered to cover the hole in my sleeve.
The queen very graciously chose not to see
The string round my trousers, the tear at my knee.
Ferdinand, Ferdinand,
Where have you been?
I've been up to London to look at the queen.
Ferdinand, Ferdinand,
What did you there?
I knelt to the queen and she touched my grey hair.

Gregory Harrison

The old woman of Clewer

There was an old woman of Clewer
Who was riding a bike and it threw her.
  A butcher came by,
  And said, 'Missus, don't cry,'
And he fastened her on with a skewer.

Anon

How to tell the top of a hill

The top of a hill
Is not until
The bottom is below.
And you have to stop
When you reach the top
For there's no more UP to go.

To make it plain
Let me explain:
The one *most* reason why
You have to stop
When you reach the top – is:
The next step up is sky.

John Ciardi

The Table and the Chair

Said the Table to the Chair,
'You can hardly be aware,
How I suffer from the heat,
And from chilblains on my feet!
If we took a little walk,
We might have a little talk!
Pray let us take the air!'
Said the Table to the Chair.

Said the Chair unto the Table,
'Now you *know* we are not able!
How foolishly you talk,
When you know we *cannot* walk!'
Said the Table with a sigh,
'It can do no harm to try,
I've as many legs as you,
Why can't we walk on two?'

So they both went slowly down,
And walked about the town
With a cheerful bumpy sound,
As they toddled round and round.
And everybody cried,
As they hastened to their side,
'See! the Table and the Chair
Have come out to take the air!'

But in going down an alley,
To a castle in the valley,
They completely lost their way,
And wandered all the day,
Till, to see them safely back,
They paid a Ducky-quack,
And a Beetle, and a Mouse,
Who took them to their house.

Then they whispered to each other,
'O delightful little brother!
What a lovely walk we've taken!
Let us dine on Beans and Bacon!'
So the Ducky and the leetle
Browny-Mousy and the Beetle
Dined, and danced upon their heads
Till they toddled to their beds.

Edward Lear

Lunch-time

If a lion you should chance to meet
When you are hurrying home to eat,
Remember when he smiles at you
That he is probably hungry too!

Barbara Ireson

Little piggy

Where are you going, you little pig?
I'm leaving my mother, I'm growing so big!
        So big, young pig!
        So young, so big!
What leaving your mother, you foolish young pig?

Where are you going, you little pig?
I've got a new spade, and I'm going to dig!
        To dig, little pig!
        A little pig dig!
Well, I never saw a pig with a spade that could dig!

Where are you going, you little pig?
Why, I'm going to have a nice ride in a gig!
        In a gig, little pig!
        What, a pig in a gig!
Well, I never yet saw a pig in a gig!

Where are you going, you little pig?
I'm going to the barber's to buy me a wig!
        A wig, little pig!
        A pig in a wig!
Why, whoever before saw a pig in a wig!

Where are you going, you little pig?
Why, I'm going to the ball to dance a fine jig!
        A jig, little pig!
        A pig dance a jig!
Well, I never before saw a pig dance a jig!

Thomas Hood

Doctor Foster

Doctor Foster went to Gloucester
  In a shower of rain;
He stepped in a puddle, up to the middle,
  And never went there again.

Anon

Oh dear

Auntie Lucy
Sat on a goosey.
Whoop – said the goosey . . .
Away flew Aunt Lucy.

Translated from a Dutch nursery
rhyme by Rose Fyleman

143

The Pobble who has no toes

The Pobble who has no toes
   Had once as many as we;
When they said, 'Some day you may lose them all,'
   He replied, – 'Fish fiddle de-dee!'
And his Aunt Jobiska made him drink,
Lavender water tinged with pink,
For she said, 'The World in general knows
There's nothing so good for a Pobble's toes!'

The Pobble who has no toes,
   Swam across the Bristol Channel;
But before he set out he wrapped his nose
   In a piece of scarlet flannel.
For his Aunt Jobiska said, 'No harm
Can come to his toes if his nose is warm;
And it's perfectly known that a Pobble's toes
Are safe, – provided he minds his nose.'

The Pobble swam fast and well,
   And when boats or ships came near him
He tinkledy-binkledy-winkled a bell,
   So that all the world could hear him.
And all the Sailors and Admirals cried,
When they saw him nearing the further side, –
'He has gone to fish, for his Aunt Jobiska's
Runcible Cat with crimson whiskers!'

But before he touched the shore,
   The shore of the Bristol Channel,
A sea-green Porpoise carried away
   His wrapper of scarlet flannel.
And when he came to observe his feet,
Formerly garnished with toes so neat,
His face at once became forlorn
On perceiving that all his toes were gone!

And nobody ever knew
    From that dark day to the present,
Whoso had taken the Pobble's toes,
    In a manner so far from pleasant.
Whether the shrimps or crawfish gray,
Or crafty Mermaids stole them away –
Nobody knew; and nobody knows
    How the Pobble was robbed of his twice five toes!

The Pobble who has no toes
    Was placed in a friendly Bark,
And they rowed him back, and carried him up,
    To his Aunt Jobiska's Park.
And she made him a feast at his earnest wish
Of eggs and buttercups fried with fish –
And she said, – 'It's a fact the whole world knows,
That Pobbles are happier without their toes.'

Edward Lear

Twenty little engines

Twenty little engines
Whistling in the yard –
One lost his whistle
And he cried SO hard

That every little engine
STOPPED in the yard
And the stationmaster ran
And BELLOWED to the guard,

'Tommy's lost his whistle,
His long, loud whistle,
And no one can shunt
When he's crying SO hard.'

The guard said, 'WHAT?'
And the guard said, 'WHO?
I've a brand new whistle
That I think will do;

'It's made of copper
And it's made of tin,
There's a hole at the bottom
Where the steam goes in;

'There's a hole at the top
Where the steam goes out,
Just like the whistle
On a tea kettle spout.

'It goes – *Peep! Peep!*
And it goes – *Hoo! Hoo!*
It's just the kind of whistle
That will do for you.'

Twenty little engines
Shunting in the sun –
Tommy got his whistle
and the work WAS DONE.

James K. Baxter

The Ombley-Gombley

Once upon a tram-line
The Ombley-Gombley sat.
Rumble clang,
Jumble bang –
And that's the end of that.

Peter Wesley-Smith

The young lady of Riga

There was a young lady of Riga
Who went out for a ride on a tiger.
    They returned from the ride
    With the lady inside
And a smile on the face of the tiger.

Anon

Spring-heeled Jack

Spring-heeled Jack
Jumped up and down
Higher than anyone
Else in the town.

The heels of his boots
Were fitted with springs;
He could fly
Like a bird with wings.

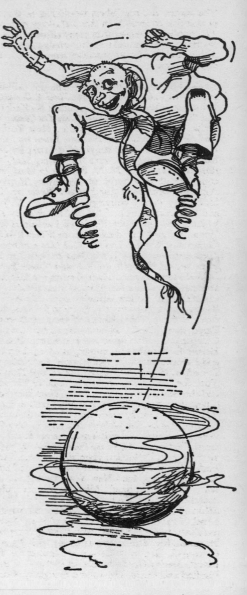

The first time up
He jumped so high
He made thunder
In the sky.

The second time up
He jumped far higher –
The North Wind set
His coat on fire.

The third time up
He jumped with zest –
The eagles plucked
His hair for a nest.

But the very last time
Spring-heeled Jack
Jumped to the moon
And never came back.

James K. Baxter

Acknowledgements

The author and publishers would like to thank the following people for giving permission to include in this anthology material which is their copyright. The publishers have made every effort to trace copyright holders. If we have inadvertently omitted to acknowledge anyone we should be most grateful if this could be brought to our attention for correction at the first opportunity.

Abelard-Schuman Limited for 'The pot calling the kettle black' and 'Pins and needles' by Pauline Clarke from *Silver Bells and Cockle Shells*. Angus and Robertson Publishers, Australia for 'Cavendish McKellar', 'Chuffa-luffa steam train' and 'The Ombley-Gombley' from *The Ombley Gombley* by Peter Wesley-Smith. Atheneum Publishers, Inc., New York for 'John' from *Let's Marry Said the Cherry and Other Nonsense Poems* by N. M. Bodecker (a Margaret K. McElderry Book), copyright © 1974 by N. M. Bodecker; 'My little dad had five little piggies' from *It's Raining Said John Twaining: Danish Nursery Rhymes Translated by N. M. Bodecker* (a Margaret K. McElderry Book), copyright © 1973 by N. M. Bodecker; 'Exploding gravy' from *One Winter Night in August and Other Nonsense Jingles* by X. J. Kennedy (a Margaret K. McElderry Book), copyright © 1975 by X. J. Kennedy; 'Ants live here' and 'Sometimes' from *I feel the Same Way* by Lilian Moore, copyright © 1967 by Lilian Moore. Basil Blackwell Publishers for 'Oh dear', 'Momotara', 'Jonathan' and 'My donkey' from *Widdy-Widdy-Wurkey* by Rose Fyleman. Chatto and Windus Ltd for 'Old Mrs Lazibones' by Gerda Mayer from *The Knockabout Show*. J. M. Dent & Sons Ltd Publishers for 'If all the hills were butter', 'What'll we do?' and 'Once there was a creepy-crawly' from *Off and Away*, rhymes adapted from the German by Brian Alderson. Dennis Dobson Publishers for 'Which' from *Good Company* by Leonard Clark and for 'The Land of the Bumbley Boo', 'Today I saw a little worm' and 'Hello Mr Python' from *Silly Verse for Kids*, 'Malice at Buckingham Palace' from *A Book of Bits*, 'Alligator' from *A Book of Milliganimals* and 'Little Pippa' from *The Little Pot Boiler*, all by Spike Milligan. Doubleday & Company, Inc. for 'In my new clothing' from *An Introduction to Haiku* by Harold G. Henderson, copyright © 1958 by Harold G. Henderson. Faber and Faber Limited for 'John' from *Let's Marry said the Cherry* by N. M. Bodecker. Faber and Faber Limited and Doubleday & Company, Inc., New York for 'The Yak', copyright 1952 by Theodore Roethke and 'The lady and the bear', copyright 1951 by Theodore Roethke, both from *The Collected Poems of Theodore Roethke*. Fontana Paperbacks for 'Dad's beard', 'My Party', 'Our hamster' and 'Dad and the cat and the tree' from *Rabbiting On* by Kit Wright. Martin Gardner for 'Cry Baby'. Greenwillow Books (a division of William Morrow & Co., New York) for 'The visitor' from *The Queen of Eeene and Other Poems* by Jack Prelutsky, copyright © 1970, 1978 by Jack Prelutsky. Hamish Hamilton Ltd for 'There's a hole in my bucket' from *Mother Goose Abroad* collected by Nicholas Tucker. Harper & Row publishers, Inc., New York for 'Afraid of the dark', 'Dreadful', 'For sale', 'It's dark in here', 'Minnow Minnie', 'Sleeping sardines' and 'Boa constrictor' from *Where the Sidewalk Ends: The Poems and Drawings of Shel Silverstein*, copyright © 1974 by Shel Silverstein and for 'I do not wish I were a cat', 'I have a friend' and 'Worm' from *Near the Window Tree: Poems and Notes by Karla Kuskin*, copyright © 1975 by Karla Kuskin. Harper's Magazine for 'The ostrich is a silly bird' by Mary E. Wilkins Freeman. George G. Harrap & Company Limited for 'Frog music' from *Mr Bidery's Spidery Garden* by David McCord. George G. Harrap & Company Limited and Little, Brown and Company, Boston, Massachusetts for 'Jam' from *Every Time I Climb a Tree* by David McCord, copyright © 1967 by David McCord. William Heinemann Ltd for 'Mr Tom Narrow' from *The Wandering Moon* by James Reeves ad for 'Hurry-scurry', 'A frog and a flea', 'The wolf couldn't catch me' and 'Halloweena Hecatee' from *Halloweena Hecatee* by Cynthia Mitchell. David Higham Associates Limited and Longmans Ltd for 'Three little puffins' by Eleanor Farjeon from *Lollipops*. Hodder & Stoughton Limited for 'If I were a fish' by Alison Winn from *Swings and Things*. Wilma Horsbrugh for 'The rocket that flew to the moon'. James Kirkup for 'There was an old man had a face made of cake'. Alfred A. Knopf, Inc., New York for 'Lambs' and 'Yes' by Mary Ann Hoberman from *Nuts to You and Nuts to Me: An Alphabet of Poems*. J. B. Lippincott, Publishers, New York for 'How to tell the top of a hill, from *The Reason for the Pelican* by John Ciardi, copyright © 1959 by John Ciardi. Little, Brown and Company, Boston, Massachusetts for 'Adventures of Isabel' from *Many Long Years Ago* by Ogden Nash, copyright © 1936 by Ogden Nash, 'Mrs Snipkin and Mrs Wobblechin' and 'Nicholas Ned' from *Tirra Lirra* by Laura E. Richards. Macmillan & Co. Ltd for 'A hamster by the name of Big Cheek' by Elizabeth Jennings from *The Secret Brother*. The Literary Trustees of Walter de la Mare and The Society of Authors as their representative for 'Miss T' and 'A – apple pie' by Walter de la Mare. Methuen Children's Books Ltd for 'Furry bear' from *Now we are Six* by A. A. Milne. Methuen Children's Books Ltd and the Canadian publishers, McClelland and Stewart Limited, Toronto, for 'Hoppity' and 'The King's breakfast' from *When We Were Very Young*, and 'The Emperor's Rhyme' from *Now We Are Six* by A. A. Milne. The Estate of Ogden Nash and Little, Brown & Co., Boston, Massachusetts, for 'The Abominable Snowman' from *You Can't Get There From Here* by Ogden Nash, copyright © 1956 by Ogden Nash, originally appeared in *The New Yorker*. Oxford University Press for 'A pig tale' from *The Blackbird in the Lilac* by James Reeves (1952) and for 'I visit the Queen' from *The Night of the Wild Horses* by Gregory Harrison (1971). Penguin Books Ltd and Atheneum Publishers for 'Lumps' from *Flashlight and Other Poems* by Judith Thurman, copyright © 1976 by Judith Thurman. Laurence Pollinger Limited and New Directions, New York, for 'Two witches' by Charles Reznikoff from *By the Waters of Manhattan*. Scott, Foresman and Company, Glenview, Illinois for 'Fair exchange' from *Up the Windy Hill* by Aileen Fisher. Charles Scribner's Sons, New York for 'The outlaw' from *At the Top of my Voice and Other Poems* by Felice Holman, copyright © 1970 by Felice Holman. Ian Serraillier for 'The tickle rhyme', © 1950 Ian Serraillier. William Jay Smith for 'The toaster', 'My body', 'People', 'Little Dimity' and 'Big Gumbo' from *Laughing Time*, published in 1955 by Atlantic Monthly/Little Brown, copyright © 1955 by William Jay Smith. The Society of Authors as the literary representative of the Estate of Rose Fyleman for 'Mrs Poff' and 'What they said' from *What They Said* by Rose Fyleman. Arnold Spilka for 'I saw a little girl I hate' from *A Rumbudgin of Nonsense*, copyright 1970. Susanna Steele for 'Skididdle, Skidaddle'. World's Work Ltd and Aileen Fisher for 'Snail's pace' and 'Daddy Longlegs' from *In the Woods, In the Meadow, In the sky* by Aileen Fisher.

Index of titles

A-apple pie *Walter de la Mare* 113

A big fat lady *Anon* 25

A farmyard song *Anon* 100

A frog and a flea *Cynthia Mitchell* 93

A grenadier *Anon* 16

A hamster by the name of Big Cheek *Elizabeth Jennings* 71

A little girl I hate *Arnold Spilka* 8

A man and his hat *Letitia Parr* 28

A mouse in her room *Anon* 88

A peanut sat on the railroad track *Anon* 54

A pig tale *James Reeves* 47

A rabbit raced a turtle *Anon* 92

A sea-serpent saw a big tanker *Anon* 56

An accident happened to my brother Jim *Anon* 53

An old grey horse stood on the wall *Anon* 76

Adventures of Isabel *Ogden Nash* 48

Afraid of the dark *Shel Silverstein* 111

Algy *Anon* 54

Alligator *Spike Milligan* 123

Ants live here *Lilian Moore* 76

At the seaside *Barbara Ireson* 137

Bandy legs *Anon* 59

Beds have legs *Barbara Ireson* 91

Big Gumbo *William Jay Smith* 23

Boa constrictor *Shel Silverstein* 55

Brother *Mary Ann Hoberman* 35

Brothers *Barbara Ireson* 40

Bushrangers *Isobel Kendall Bowden* 26

Cavendish McKellar *Peter Wesley-Smith* 24

Chuffa-luffa steam train *Peter Wesley-Smith* 136

Cry-baby *Martin Gardner* 9

Dad and the cat and the tree *Kit Wright* 32

Daddy longlegs *Aileen Fisher* 77

Dad's beard *Kit Wright* 42

Deborah Delora *Anon* 25

Dickery, dickery, dare *Anon* 76

Dicky Dan *Anon* 20

Did you ever go fishing? *Anon* 56

Doctor Foster *Anon* 43

Dogs can't talk *Anon* 90

Dreadful *Shel Silverstein* 44

Exploding gravy *X. J. Kennedy* 126

Fair exchange *Aileen Fisher* 109

Five little piggies *Translated from a Danish nursery rhyme by N. M. Bodecker* 39

Five little squirrels *Anon* 66

Five tiny green peas *Anon* 80

For sale *Shel Silverstein* 41

Froggy Boggy *Anon* 63

Frog music *David McCord* 64

Funny little man *Barbara Ireson* 45

Furry bear *A. A. Milne* 108

Fuzzy Wuzzy *Anon* 74

Goosey, goosey gander *Anon* 66

Granny in the kitchen *Anon* 43

Halloweena Hecatee *Cynthia Mitchell* 121

Have you ever? *Barbara Ireson* 128

Have you heard of the man?
Anon 22

Hello, Mr Python *Spike Milligan*
70

Here's a story *Anon* 51

Hicketty picketty *Anon* 96

Hinx, minx *Anon* 96

Homes for rent *Barbara Ireson*
90

Hoppity *A. A. Milne* 135

How to tell the top of a hill
John Ciardi 139

Hurry-Scurry *Cynthia Mitchell*
20

I do not wish I were a cat *Karla
Kuskin* 111

I eat my peas with honey *Anon*
129

I had a little dóg *Anon* 74

I have a friend *Karla Kuskin* 39

I once saw an ant as big as a
mouse *John Cunliffe* 82

I visit the queen *Gregory Harrison*
138

I went downtown *Anon* 136

I wish I were a little grub *Anon*
99

If all the hills were butter
*Translated from the German by
Brian Alderson* 127

If I were a fish *Alison Winn* 108

I'm just going out for a moment
Mike Rosen 119

Inketty minketty monketty
muddle *Anon* 57

In my new clothing *Japanese
poem by Bashō, translated by
Harold G. Henderson* 98

In the park *Barbara Ireson* 104

It's dark in here *Shel Silverstein*
52

Jam *David McCord* 124

Jeremiah Obadiah *Anon* 121

Jerry and Mandy *Variation on an
old rhyme by Barbara Ireson* 24

John N. M. Bodecker 12

John Bull *Anon* 121

Jolly Roger *Anon* 122

Jonathan *Rose Fyleman* 49

Lambs *Mary Ann Hoberman* 69

Little Dimity *William Jay Smith*
18

Little piggy *Thomas Hood* 142

Little Pippa *Spike Milligan* 51

Little Sammy Soapsuds *Anon*
55

Lumps *Judith Thurman* 91

Lunch-time *Barbara Ireson* 141

Malice at Buckingham Palace
Spike Milligan 124

Michael Finnegan *Anon* 86

Milkman, milkman *Anon* 53

Min *Barbara Ireson* 68

Minnow Minnie *Shel Silverstein*
51

Miss T. *Walter de la Mare* 128

Momotara *Translated from the
Japanese by Rose Fyleman* 92

Mrs Poff *Translated from the
German by Rose Fyleman* 56

Mrs Snipkin and Mrs
Wobblechin *Laura Richards*
58

Mr Green's story *Barbara Ireson*
131

Mr Tom Narrow *James Reeves*
38

My body *William Jay Smith* 98

My donkey *Translated from a
French nursery rhyme by Rose
Fyleman* 65

My first suitor *Anon* 16

My party *Kit Wright* 36

My toaster *Barbara Ireson* 117

Neighbours *Barbara Ireson* 34

Never say to a bat *Barbara Ireson* 67

New shoes *Anon* 103

Nicholas Ned *Laura Richards* 85

Oh dear *Translated from a Dutch nursery rhyme by Rose Fyleman* 143

Old Mrs Lazibones *Gerda Mayer* 27

Once there was a creepy-crawly *Translated from the German by Brian Alderson* 84

One day a boy went walking *Anon* 82

Our hamster *Kit Wright* 72

Our little dog *Anon* 63

Peas for breakfast *Michael Rosen* 125

People *William Jay Smith* 22

Pepper and salt *Barbara Ireson* 123

Peter and Michael *Anon* 90

Pete's sweets *Eve Merriam* 127

Pillykin, Willykin, Winkey Wee *Anon* 117

Pinch me, Punch me and Tread-on-my-toes *Anon* 81

Pins and needles *Pauline Clarke* 107

Poppleton to Pippleton *Barbara Ireson* 132

Poor elephant *Barbara Ireson* 71

Queen, Queen Caroline *Anon* 9

Railway navvy *Anon* 120

Riddle-me, riddle-me rumpty *Anon* 52

Robert Rowley *Anon* 123

Robin the Bobbin *Anon* 18

Round the lake *Anon* 70

Said the monkey to the donkey *Anon* 85

Saturday night *Anon* 43

Seven fat fishermen *Anon* 21

Simple Simon *Anon* 59

Sing-song *Barbara Ireson* 99

Skididdle, skidaddle *Susanna Steele* 23

Sleeping sardines *Shel Silverstein* 120

Snail's pace *Aileen Fisher* 77

Snakes *Barbara Ireson* 78

Sometimes *Lilian Moore* 98

Spring-heeled Jack *James K. Baxter* 148

Sue, Sue *Barbara Ireson* 20

Sulky Sue *Anon* 8

The abominable snowman *Ogden Nash* 22

The alligator *Mary Macdonald* 93

The diner at Crewe *Anon* 125

The elephant *Anon* 87

The Elephant *John Joy Bell* 45

The elephant carries a great big trunk *Anon* 69

The Emperor's rhyme *A. A. Milne* 14

The fat man of Bombay *Anon* 17

The fly *Anon* 75

The girl in the lane *Anon* 16

The hungry hunter *Anon* 60

The indignant male *A. B. Ross* 106

The King's breakfast *A. A. Milne* 114

The Lady and the Bear *Theodore Roethke* 50

The Land of the Bumbley Boo *Spike Milligan* 83

The lizard *Anon* 67

The old man of Peru *Anon* 118

The Old Man on the Border *Edward Lear* 19

The old man with a beard
Edward Lear 11

The Old Person Edward Lear
126

The Old Person of Ickley
Edward Lear 131

The Old Person of Ware
Edward Lear 132

The Old Person of Wilts
Edward Lear 133

The old woman of Clewer Anon
139

The Ombley-Gombley Peter
Wesley-Smith 147

The ostrich is a silly bird Mary
E. Wilkins Freeman 89

The outlaw Felice Holman 80

The pasty Anon 43

The Pobble who has no toes
Edward Lear 144

The pot calling the kettle black
Pauline Clarke 88

The rocket that flew to the
moon Wilma Horsbrugh 134

The Table and the Chair
Edward Lear 140

The telephone and the door-bell
Barbara Ireson 86

The three cooks Anon 54

The tickle rhyme Ian Serraillier
87

The toaster William Jay Smith
113

The visitor Jack Prelutsky 31

The way to the zoo Anon 10

The wolf couldn't catch me
Cynthia Mitchell 68

The Yak Theodore Roethke 75

The young lady of Riga Anon 147

The Young Lady whose chin
Edward Lear 19

The Young Lady whose nose
Edward Lear 10

The young man of Bengal
Anon 47

There's a hole in my bucket
German nursery rhyme 61

There was a crooked man Anon
13

There was a king Anon 117

There was a little dog Anon 69

There was an old man James
Kirkup 60

There were three ghostesses
Anon 84

Three little puffins Eleanor
Farjeon 129

Three young rats Anon 95

Through the teeth Anon 118

Tiger Mary Ann Hoberman 67

Timothy Titus Anon 11

Tip-top Micheal Rosen 120

Today I saw a little worm
Spike Milligan 78

Toeses Anon 85

To market ride the gentlemen
Anon 137

Tony Baloney Dennis Lee 10

Twenty little engines James K.
Baxter 146

Twiddle-di-dee, twiddle-di-dee
Traditional 133

Two witches Alexander Reznikoff
13

Up in the North Anon 86

Well I never Anon 94

What is the rhyme for
porringer? Anon 21

What'll we do? Translated from
the German by Brian Alderson
81

What's in the cupboard? Anon
122

What they said Translated from a
German nursery rhyme by Rose
Fyleman 94

Whenever there's snow *Barbara Ireson* 103

When I went out for a walk one day *Anon* 109

Which *Leonard Clark* 110

Who's that ringing at my door bell? *Anon* 70

Worm *Karla Kuskin* 78

Yes *Mary Ann Hoberman* 105

Index of first lines

A cry-baby whimpers wherever she goes 9

A diner while dining at Crewe 125

A frog and a flea 93

A hamster by the name of Big Cheek 71

A Lady came to a Bear by a Stream 50

A little man I used to see 45

A lizard wriggled on his belly 67

A mouse in her room woke Miss Dowd 88

A peanut sat on the railroad track 54

A rabbit raced a turtle 92

A scandalous man 40

A sea-serpent saw a big tanker 56

A silver-scaled Dragon with jaws flaming red 113

Algy saw a bear 54

An accident happened to my brother Jim 53

An old grey horse stood on the wall 76

Andrew is my brother 40

Ants live here 76

As I was going to sell my eggs 59

As I was walking round the lake 70

Auntie Lucy 143

Aunt Mary is my aunt 45

Beds have legs, but cannot walk 91

'Bubble!' said the pot 88

Cavendish McKellar 24

Christopher Columbus! 25

Christopher Robin goes 135

Chuffa-luffa steam train 136

Deborah Delora, she liked a bit of fun 25

Deedle, deedle dumpling, my son John, 43

Dickery, dickery, dare 76

Dicky Dan was a funny old man 20

Did you ever go fishing on a bright sunny day 56

Doctor Foster went to Gloucester 143

'Dogs can't talk!' I told my puppy 90

Don't you think a daddy longlegs 77

Ferdinand, Ferdinand 138

Fifty burly bushrangers 26

Five little squirrels sat up in a tree 66

Five tiny green peas lying in a row 80

Froggy Boggy 63

From Sydney Zoo 123

Fuzzy Wuzzy was a bear 74

Goosey, goosey gander 66

Granny in the kitchen 43

Great big gawky Gumbo Cole 23

Halloweena Hecatee 121

Have you ever spread jam on ham? 128

Have you heard of the man 22

Hello, Mr Python 70

'Here, brown these' 117

Here is a rocket that flew to the moon 134

Here's a story 51

Here's Sulky Sue 8

Hicketty picketty, pizer jiggitty 96
Hinx, minx, the old Witch winks 96
Hour after hour 22
Humps are lumps 91
Hurry-scurry 20

I am writing these lines 52
I do not wish I were a cat 111
I eat my peas with honey 129
I had a cat and my cat pleased me 100
I had a little brother 35
I had a little dog, his name was Ball 74
I have a friend who keeps standing on her hands 39
I once saw an ant as big as a mouse 82
I peppered my fish and salted my chips 123
I saw a little girl I hate 8
I went downtown 136
I went to the park today 104
I went to the sea and what did I see? 137
I wish I were a little grub 99
If a lion you should chance to meet 141
If all the hills were butter 127
If I were a bear 108
If only the rabbits 90
I'll give a candle 109
I'm a navvy, you're a navvy 120
I'm a tiger 67
I'm just going out for a moment 119
I'm Reginald Clark. I'm afraid of the dark 111
I'm sorry for old elephant 71
'I'm tired of eating just beans,' says I 120

In a boggy old bog 64
Inketty minketty monketty muddle 57
In my new clothing 98
In the Land of the Bumbley Boo 83
Into the house of a Mrs MacGruder 80
Isabel met an enormous bear 48
it came today to visit 31
It's a very odd thing 128
It's four o'clock 94
I've got a dog 68
I've never seen an abominable snowman 22

Jeremiah Obadiah, puff, puff, puff 121
Jerry Hall 24
John Bull, John Bull 121
John could take his clothes off 12
Jolly Roger lived up a tree 122
Jonathan Gee 49

Lambs are full of curly wool 69
Last year my Dad grew a great big thick red beard 42
Little fly upon the wall 75
Little Jack Dandy-prat 16
Little Pollie Pillikins 113

Maybe it's so 77
May I ask you if you've noticed 51
Milkman, milkman, where have you been? 53
Moses supposes 85
Mr Mauve walked out one day 131
Mrs Down 34
My donkey, my dear 65
My little 39

My mother's big green gravy boat 126

My parents said I could have a party 36

My shoes are new and squeaky shoes 183

Never say to a bat 67

Nicholas Ned 85

O dear, O dear 107

Oh I'm being eaten by a boa constrictor 55

Oh, Pillykin, Willykin, Winkey Weel 117

Old Mrs Lazibones 27

Once upon a tram-line 147

Once there was a creepy-crawly 84

One day a boy went walking 82

One sister for sale! 41

On Saturday night I lost my wife 43

On the Mount of Bolliboff 56

Our hamster's life 72

Our little dog 63

Outside Buckingham Palace 124

peas for breakfast please he said 125

Pete 127

Peter and Michael were two little menikin 90

Pinch me, Punch me and Tread-on-my-toes 81

Pip Pip Pippety Pip 51

Poor Jane Higgins 47

Poor little pigeon-toed Dimity Drew 18

Queen, Queen Caroline 9

Riddle-me, riddle-me rumpty 52

Ring, ring, ring . . . 86

Robert Rowley rolled a round roll round 123

Robin the Bobbin, the big fat Ben 18

Said the monkey to the donkey 85

Said the Table to the Chair 140

Seven fat fisherman 21

Simple Simon went a-fishing 59

Skididdle 23

Skinny Mrs Snipkin 58

Snakes I can take or leave 78

Someone ate the baby 44

Sometimes 98

Splash, splosh! 108

'Spread,' said Toast to Butter 124

Spring-heeled Jack 148

Sue, Sue, what would you do 20

That's the way to the zoo 10

The alligator chased his tail 93

The elephant carries a great big trunk 69

The elephant is a graceful bird 87

The girl in the lane 16

The King asked 114

The King of Peru 14

The ostrich is a silly bird 89

The people of Poppleton 132

The Pobble who has no toes 144

The top of a hill 139

The way they scrub 106

The wolf couldn't catch me 68

There's a hole in my bucket, dear Conrad, dear Conrad 61

There was a crooked man, and he walked a crooked mile 13

There was a fat man of Bombay 17

There was a hungry hunter 60
There was a king who had four sons 117
There was a little dog and he had a little tail 69
There was a most odious Yak 75
There was an old man 28
There was an old man 60
There was an old man of Peru 118
There was an Old Man on the Border 19
There was an old man named Michael Finnegan 86
There was an old man with a beard 11
There was an Old Person of Ickley 131
There was an Old Person of Ware 132
There was an Old Person of Wilts 133
There was an Old Person whose habits 126
There was an old woman of Clewer 139
There was a witch 13
There was a young lady of Riga 147
There was a Young Lady whose chin 19
There was a Young Lady whose nose 10
There was a young man of Bengal 47
There were three ghostesses 84
There were two cooks from Colebrook 54
This is a song 99

This morning a cat got 32
Three little puffins 129
Three young rats with black felt hats 95
Through the teeth 118
Timothy Titus took two ties 11
Tip-top, tip-top 120
Today I saw a little worm 78
To market ride the gentlemen 137
Tony Baloney is fibbing again 10
Twenty little engines 146
Twiddle-di-dee, twiddle-di-dee 133
Up in the North, a long way off 86
Well I never, did you ever 94
What is the rhyme for porringer? 21
What'll we do? 81
What's in the cupboard? 122
Whenever there's snow 103
When I went out for a walk one day 109
When little Sammy Soapsuds 55
Where are you going, you little pig? 142
Where did Momotara go 92
Wherever I go, it also goes 98
Who comes here? 16
Who's that ringing at my door bell? 70
'Who's that tickling my back?' said the wall 87
Worm 78
Would you rather be 110
Yes 105

BEAVER BOOKS FOR YOUNGER READERS

Have you heard about all the exciting stories available in Beaver? You can buy them in bookstores or they can be ordered directly from us. Just complete the form below and send the right amount of money and the books will be sent to you at home.

☐	THE BIRTHDAY KITTEN	Enid Blyton	£1.50
☐	THE WISHING CHAIR AGAIN	Enid Blyton	£1.99
☐	BEWITCHED BY THE BRAIN SHARPENERS	Philip Curtis	£1.75
☐	SOMETHING NEW FOR A BEAR TO DO	Shirley Isherwood	£1.95
☐	REBECCA'S WORLD	Terry Nation	£1.99
☐	CONRAD	Christine Nostlinger	£1.50
☐	FENELLA FANG	Ritchie Perry	£1.95
☐	MRS PEPPERPOT'S OUTING	Alf Prøysen	£1.99
☐	THE WORST KIDS IN THE WORLD	Barbara Robinson	£1.75
☐	THE MIDNIGHT KITTENS	Dodie Smith	£1.75
☐	ONE GREEN BOTTLE	Hazel Townson	£1.50
☐	THE VANISHING GRAN	Hazel Townson	£1.50
☐	THE GINGERBREAD MAN	Elizabeth Walker	£1.50
☐	BOGWOPPIT	Ursula Moray Williams	£1.95

If you would like to order books, please send this form, and the money due to:
ARROW BOOKS, BOOKSERVICE BY POST, PO BOX 29, DOUGLAS, ISLE OF MAN, BRITISH ISLES. Please enclose a cheque or postal order made out to Arrow Books Ltd for the amount due including 22p per book for postage and packing both for orders within the UK and for overseas orders.

NAME ....

ADDRESS ....

....

Please print clearly.

Whilst every effort is made to keep prices low it is sometimes necessary to increase cover prices at short notice. Arrow Books reserve the right to show new retail prices on covers which may differ from those previously advertised in the text or elsewhere.